GETTING SOBER...
AND
• LOVING IT! •
in association with SHARP

Joan and Derek Taylor

VERMILION
LONDON

To 'The Children'

Published in 1992 by Vermilion
an imprint of Ebury Press
Random Century House
20 Vauxhall Bridge Road
London SW1V 2SA

Catalogue record for this book is available
from the British Library.

ISBN 0 09 175 87 X

Designed by: Chris Warner
Edited by: Gillian Haslam

Typeset in Garamond by SX Composing Ltd, Rayleigh, Essex
Printed in Great Britain by Mackays of Chatham Plc, Kent

ABOUT THE AUTHORS

Joan and Derek Taylor have been married since 1958 and are both Merseyside-born. After a period as a journalist, Derek worked as the Beatles press officer during the 1960s He then became managing director of Warner Bros (UK) and vice-president of Warner Bros (US). He dropped out in the late 1970s to write books and concentrate on the family. Joan has brought up their three daughters and three sons and is now a Citizen's Advice Bureau worker. Joan and Derek now have two grandsons and are happily settled in an old mill on a river in Suffolk.

CONTENTS

An alcoholic is a sick person needing to be well, not a bad person needing to be good.

Dr Brian Wells

ACKNOWLEDGEMENTS

In preparing this book we have been indebted to and couldn't have made it without our generous and honest interviewees: fellow travellers in the vale of tears, now at some kind of destination. Call it Recovery. The news is good for all who have got sober. We all love it a lot more than the alternative.

So, thanks to all seventeen recovering alcoholics who are featured in this book who spoke to us and to the others who gave their time, strength, hope and experience. Thanks, too, to Alcoholics Anonymous and Al-Anon for the rescue operation that brought us to recovery. Much thanks, credit and honour to Rowena Webb of Vermilion, our friend and guide. Thanks, too, to all of the following: Mark Bennett, Jill Wetton, Deirdre Gordon, Sue Norman, Linda Gleason, Reg Davis-Poynter, Vanessa Taylor, Libby Taylor, Keren Levy, Gillian Haslam, Fiona MacIntyre, Sue Cousins, Olivia Harrison, Brian Roylance, and the late George Hoy Booth. Our thanks also go to NEL, Jimmy Greaves and Norman Giller for permission to quote from *This One's On Me* by Jimmy Greaves and *It's A Funny Old Life* by Jimmy Greaves and Norman Giller.

Throughout, we have been supported by – and have leaned on – Emma Gibbs and Brian Wells of SHARP – special places on the top table for them. We send love and gratitude to Richard and Barbara Starkey for putting us up to it in the first place. Finally, we thank each other. God grant us all the serenity to accept the things we cannot change, the courage to change the things we can and wisdom to know the difference.

Joan and Derek Taylor
Suffolk, 1992

· FOREWORD ·
by
Ringo Starr and Barbara Bach

$\diamond$

As we have both been rescued from addiction by attendance at a self-help treatment centre, we're very happy to write a foreword to this book which has been written in conjunction with SHARP (Self Help Addiction Recovery Programme).

SHARP was started by Dr Brian Wells who has himself been in treatment for addiction to alcohol as well as other substances, and his story is in this book along with many others who have got help, got sober and are now enjoying their lives in recovery, one day at a time.

Getting Sober ... and Loving It! shows how to get that recovery and keep it. Addiction is a disease, not a moral failing, and the only way to deal with it is first to admit you have it and then decide to go after recovery. The great advantage in accepting there is a problem is that, after the surrender, you can grow in awareness and have a far, far better life.

It isn't all doom and gloom and ginger ale. Our own experience of treatment is that you have to be sick to want recovery. You are in a fog which starts to lift after you put down the drink or drug. At first you are on a pink cloud. Sober at last! Then you have to start work on yourself, you can close the chapter and start a new one. You will hear in treatment that 'it's a selfish programme' and you think 'I'm not going to get involved in a selfish programme', but you realise that you are simply being asked to take care of yourself and let other people look after themselves. *It's self-help, in treatment.*

You can work out your resentments and find out where all this started, when (and maybe why) you had your first drink. You will see in the stories in this book that we all have a lot in common. You can *identify* with other people and realise that you are not alone – there is a place where you can get help, and there are people who are happy to share with you their own experience, strength and hope.

In our own case, we needed something big like addiction to come into our lives to knock us down and make us realise that a total change was necessary. We needed something to bring us to our knees, and make us do something about ourselves.

Others in the book will share the pain of addiction with you and how they gained through acknowledging it. All the pain and wreckage of our past is now serving us well, standing us in good stead. *There really is no gain without pain.* Like a lot of truth, it sounds trite but it is clear to see. It's hard for us to understand how people who haven't gone through that pain manage their lives because in recovery programmes you find you *can* manage your life, one day at a time. When things get really difficult you can think 'It *will* pass today.' If something happens that we really don't like, the bottom line is we won't feel like this forever.

You find you don't have to live with fear and denial any longer. You can face up to your problems and learn acceptance. Accept yourself and other people.

One wonderful thing for us in treatment was that at the outset we were treated like everybody else. Like Rich and Barb. There was no Ringo and Miss Bach. We were right in there with everyone else and it was so great not to be singled out. Simple things became a pleasure again. When we go out now we have such a fabulous time, and we make plans and keep them. As we go past bars we remember that in the old days the bar is as far as we would have gone, at nine in the morning and right through the day.

When we go on holidays now, we don't hide away. We used to go on long plane journeys, rent huge villas, stock up the bars, hide and get deranged. Now we don't have to go through all of that. We're free to have normal, happy family holidays with no compulsions to feed. In our everyday lives, we are aware of our real commitment to each other without having to do all the same things together at the same time which is how it was before, in a state of codependency, which is very common in addiction.

Nothing that we experience in recovery will come as a surprise to other recovering addicts. As we've said, the strength of getting sober and loving it lies in the power to identify with others; no matter where they come from or what they've experienced, if they're compulsive users of whatever, there is so much in common it's amazing. It's just great to be able to see so clearly.

It's true that most people aren't substance-addicts. We were at our friends' wedding in Fiji. It started at 11 am and we were still hanging around at five that night. We were laughing and chatting with another member of a fellowship of recovering addicts, and we were just so surprised that no-one had tried to pull someone else's wife, no-one had taken off his sarong or danced on the table. These people were *social* drinkers.

Maybe *you* are just a social drinker, like the majority of people. If so, fine. But if you're not, or if somebody you love is having problems . . . then this book is for you.

· INTRODUCTION ·
by
Dr Brian Wells
Consultant Psychiatrist and Medical Director of SHARP

⸻ ◇ ⸻

SHARP (The Self Help Addiction Recovery Programme) was started because of need – the need to provide treatment that some of us are highly confident about, and the need to show sceptics that treatment based on the twelve steps can be cheap and highly effective.

SHARP provides an intensive day treatment programme for people who have become addicted to and dependent on alcohol and/or mind-altering drugs. The programme is based on the understanding that alcoholism and addiction is an illness. Daily abstinence provides the cornerstone of recovery for the individual and their family members. Attendance at and application to the principles of the self-help groups Alcoholics Anonymous, Narcotics Anonymous and the corresponding family groups is strongly encouraged. As a result of the twelve steps suggested by AA, the treatment is sometimes referred to as 'twelve step-based', or the Minnesota Model.

Twelve step treatment in the UK is viewed by most specialists as old-fashioned, 'American' and likely to be useful for either those with a religious background, or the socially advantaged. The inclusion of this latter group comes about, firstly, as a result of publicity from the USA (mainly the Betty Ford Centre), which often involved a number of wealthy and high profile patients. Secondly, when twelve step treatment began in this country, it was impossible for the agencies involved (Broadway Lodge, Clouds House, etc) to get adequate funding. Consequently, they were obliged to take in fee-paying patients at private sector rates. The fact that these fees offset the cost of the remaining majority of patients (who effectively received free treatment) did little to dissuade professionals that Minnesota Model treatment was anything other than an expensive resource for the rich. When approaches were made for government funding, the reply was always the same. 'Show me the research.' 'There is no hard evidence to demonstrate the usefulness of this form of treatment.' 'Don't tell me, show me!'

The situation was not helped by a number of treatment agencies who made frankly outrageous success claims as part of their marketing strategies. Glossy brochures appeared containing statements such as 'We have a ninety percent success rate'. Such claims, many of which said nothing about how the patient was selected, how many of them failed to complete the course and what happened to those that did drop out, were like a red flag to the highly critical professionals, who have chosen to ignore the fact that few of the treatment modalities, including those which they practise, have been adequately researched either.

Research in this field is expensive, takes a long time and often produces results that are difficult to make clear statements about. It is relatively easy to research methadone maintenance, use of Antabuse and electric shock 'aversion' treatment, as one is treating relatively 'captive' populations. Active drinkers and drug takers move around, go abroad, arrive at different hospitals and all too frequently die. It is difficult to apply laboratory principles to this form of human behaviour.

So there we were, in central London, in 1988. The only money available was that provided (very importantly) to prevent the spread of HIV. AA and NA were plentiful, but to try to provide twelve step treatment in such a political climate was a non-starter. We decided therefore to do it ourselves, to set up a charity in order to provide free treatment which would fill a vital gap, and be the subject of a controlled research study, performed by independent, non-biased, professional researchers.

We teamed up with The Chemical Dependency Centre (CDC). They were already providing an out-patient service, after-care and half-way houses for people who had been through primary treatment. A primary care day programme was an obvious next step for them. They were already an established charity with an excellent Board of Trustees, so we agreed that SHARP could become an independent project within the body of CDC. Our fund raising efforts would be separate to theirs, as would our clinical work, albeit with obvious areas of overlap. The fund raising began.

We went to North America and received a great deal of encouragement from legends in the field such as Dan Anderson, Gordy Grimm, Anne Geller and Nick Colangelo. It became clear that if we were successful, we would have an opportunity to provide necessary treatment and to conduct a research project that is virtually impossible to do in the United States. The system of health care and the geography make it impossible for, say, Hazelden, to attempt a controlled study, comparing itself with a facility that offers a different model of treatment.

Back in the UK, Emma Gibbs got to work. She wrote to charitable trusts, grant-making organisations, wealthy individuals and virtually anyone she could think of. Old contacts were renewed, fund raising events were sponsored and old boyfriends were blackmailed! Gradually the money started to trickle in. Charity Projects made a generous donation and we were then able to point to some success in order to generate more. What we had not counted on, however, was the overwhelming support that we received from the recovering community.

Barbara Bach became Chairperson of our Fund Raising Committee and our list of friends grew. Fund raising dinners were organised, Barry Humphries gave us a wonderful exclusive evening at The Waldorf Hotel (as Dame Edna) and individuals donated in a way we could not have hoped for (including Bill O'Donnell of Sierra Tucson who flew to the UK in order to present his generous cheque). The reality of SHARP came about after receiving a major donation from The Stone Foundation, following which our Trustees announced we were now in a position to open as we had raised two-thirds of our target.

SHARP is now open and it is still very early days. The last four years have been at times exciting and tremendous fun, at others frustrating and filled with despair. The work has begun and we need to get it right. We have an excellent team of trained people on board. Now we need to work together to provide a treatment centre that we can all be proud of. Evaluation and research have been taking place from the outset and as Barbara said after her fund raising appearance on Wogan, 'now it's up to you guys'.

It is too early to be self-congratulatory, or to recommend that others should try to do the same. Fund raising for addictions is a tough business, however should the research demonstrate that SHARP is cost-efficient, there will be data that others can use in order to apply for funding from more established sources.

There have been far too many people and organisations involved to thank individually, but special mention must go to our Fund Raising Committee which continues to do battle, Tristan Millington-Drake and the Trustees of CDC for their continued support, and of course Emma Gibbs. In particular, special thanks are due to Joan and

Derek Taylor for their extremely hard work in putting together this book. I do hope that it will be widely read and that the individual stories will be enjoyed, understood and taken note of.

Alcoholism and 'addiction' are highly treatable illnesses. There is no such thing as a hopeless case, and once recovery begins, the results can be spectacular. The following pages demonstrate this vividly.

· PART ONE ·

The good news is that if you like a couple of drinks now and then, or even most days, you needn't worry about your drinking. That applies to most of us.

Alcohol is a pal, a life enhancer, soother of grief and cheerful companion. It is a sedative drug that in small to moderate doses causes a sense of well-being, liveliness and a lessening of inhibition. Taken in sensible amounts and at the right time and in the right place, it provides an enormous number of people with a great deal of pleasure. It plays an important part in our social and cultural life. What's more, the production and distribution of alcohol pours a significant amount of money into our economy. So alcohol scores highly on the register of Good Things and in many ways Britain would be much poorer without it. (Imagine Christmas!)

The bad news is that about seven million people in this country are regularly drinking alcohol over recommended safe limits. Drinking the wrong amount at the wrong time can lead to immeasurable harm. Too much on a single occasion reduces concentration and restraint which can lead to accidents and anti-social behaviour. Excessive consumption over long periods causes physical and mental damage.

This book is primarily aimed at people who regularly step out of their brains and whose lives have become unmanageable. It is also intended as a friend in need for those who are close to such people, whose own lives have become affected by heavy drinking.

If you are wondering if all or any of this applies to you, read on. This book is a good map through a minefield; all of us who tell our stories are recovering drunkards or have first-hand knowledge of life with such people.

Hope – and help – is at hand.

The statistics of drinking

The following lists of facts and figures illustrate just how widespread and how horrific the effects of alcoholism have become.

- 1,400,000 people in the UK are drinking at levels regarded as harmful to health.
- One in four men and one in twelve women drink more than the recommended sensible levels.

Alcohol is involved in:
- One third of all domestic accidents.
- Up to 62% of all serious head injuries.
- One fifth of drownings (more than one third in the 25-29 age group).
- One in five child abuse cases.
- More than a third of deaths in fires.
- At least one in five murders. (Some research places the figure at more than half of all murders.)

On the roads:
- Around 800 people are killed each year in accidents where at least one driver or rider is over the legal alcohol limit.
- About one in five drivers and motorcyclists killed in road accidents have alcohol levels above the legal limits.
- 60% of drivers and riders killed on Friday and Saturday nights, whose blood alcohol levels are known, are found to be over the legal limit.
- Between 10.00 pm and 4.00 am, 80% of pedestrians killed, whose blood alcohol levels are known, are over the legal limit for drivers.
- An increase of 260% in women convicted of drinking and driving has been noted between 1975 and 1988. The increase for men in that period was 62.5%.
- Drinking and driving costs around £630 million every year, including costs to the NHS.

Criminal statistics show:
- There were 92,820 convictions or cuations in 1989 for drunkenness offences. This figure has doubled since the 1950s.
- In 1983 45% of cases of wounding were committed by people thought by their victims to have been drinking.

- Almost half the incidents of disorderly behaviour dealt with by the police occur shortly after the end of permitted hours for licensed premises and are more likely to occur on Friday or Saturday nights and to involve young men.
- 9% of the adult males, 9% of the young males and 4% of the females in the prison population are clinically diagnosed as alcohol-dependent and the government suggests that 'perhaps as many as half drink more than the recommended sensible limits'.

Among the young:
- Half the eleven year olds surveyed in 1989 said they had drunk the previous week.
- Four out of five teenage drinkers report adverse consequences after drinking.
- 1,000 children under fifteen are admitted to hospital each year with acute alcoholic poisoning.
- Of the 100 people who die every year of direct alcohol poison, some are children.
- Convictions for drunkenness among teenagers have more than tripled in thirty years.

In the workplace:
- At least eight million days are lost each year to alcohol-related sickness absence – more than twice the number lost through industrial action.
- Alcohol-related problems are estimated to have cost British industry about £1,700 million in 1987. This does *not* take account of certain costs such as reduced efficiency, lost production and industrial accidents.
- A study has demonstrated that one in five industrial accident victims in one UK plant had admitted drinking prior to the accident.

That's not *all* the bad news but it is enough to suggest alcohol doesn't come into our culture trouble-free.

And the upside:
- In 1989 the alcohol industry in the UK contributed £6.5 billion (around 1.5%) to Gross Domestic Product. In 1990, exports of Scotch whisky were worth over £1.7 billion (nearly 1.7% of all UK exports).
- About 60,000 people were employed in the alcohol industry in

1990 and a further 350,000 were employed in the distribution and sale of alcohol.
- Alcohol contributed nearly £7 billion to government revenues in 1989; just under two thirds in excise duty and just over one third in VAT.

In general, it is accepted that the cause of the great rise in consumption of alcohol in the last thirty years is due to affluence – the price of alcohol in real terms in relation to disposable income is almost half what it was thirty years ago.

The difference between a social drinker and an alcoholic

In spite of the dangers of excess, normal drinking is part of an acceptable pattern of social behaviour, and though occasionally normal drinkers use alcohol to deal with stress or difficult emotions, this is unlikely to become a habit. *Normal drinkers can take it or leave it*. In British life many people are social drinkers.

- Light social drinkers have a pint of beer or a glass of wine occasionally, maybe at weekends, on holiday or at weddings, funerals or Christmas. This is the sort of drinker who worries no one except the alcoholic, the lofty compulsive drinker who can't understand how such people can possibly enjoy life.
- A moderate social drinker might like a glass of wine or two or a couple of pints three or four times a week, yet stays within the limits of 'sensible drinking'. There doesn't seem too much to worry about here and there are in Britain millions of moderate social drinkers.

And then there is the heavy social drinker who drinks quite a lot, with more at times when there's social pressure, business stress or a Big Day.

- Heavy social drinkers will probably drink every day, two or three pints a day, add a few glasses of wine and a large Scotch here and there, and think nothing of it. They are not necessarily problem drinkers except that they may well be sustaining physical damage.

Occasionally these drinkers get a little drunk or maybe a lot drunk, but as it doesn't happen too often and the partner doesn't mind too much, the job is secure, the family's affairs are quite together and there hasn't been any negative breathalysing, no one worries.

The fact is that alcohol is a wonderful friend to lots of people and what separates the social drinker from the alcoholic is this distinction: *social* drinkers, whether light, moderate or heavy, can give up drinking if they want to; the *alcoholic* can't.

The only way an alcoholic can stay away from alcohol is by refraining from having the *next* drink. A heavy social drinker who does not have the problem of compulsion *can* say 'I've had enough.' An alcoholic who is still active has *never* had enough. It's said, in fact, that one drink is too many and a thousand are not enough.

The social drinkers in all three categories can all *progress* to alcoholism in due course if their drinking becomes compulsive. Nobody knows what causes alcoholism, what it is that makes one man or woman, boy or girl able to tolerate alcohol, take it or leave it and yet another just as clever, apparently healthy, successful, quite incapable of stopping when things get out of hand.

Remember, this book is not anti-alcohol. We realise that alcohol is a good companion in light to moderate amounts for the majority of drinkers. Heavy social drinkers can decide for themselves whether or not, by exceeding the medically-established safety limits, they wish to risk damaging their health.

What is an alcoholic?

The word 'alcoholism' is now considered by the medical profession to be too imprecise. It is a word first coined in the late 1840s to describe the overall condition suffered by people who habitually drink alcohol to an excessive degree and who, in consequence, have special problems.

The World Health Organisation states that alcoholics are excessive drinkers whose dependence on alcohol has reached such a level that they show noticeable mental disturbances, interference with their bodily health, their interpersonal relations and their smooth economic and social functioning.

Chronic alcoholism is recognised by the American Medical Association as a disease. The victim cannot voluntarily abstain for more than a short while. It is a threefold disease which harms the drinker mentally, physically and spiritually. Some professionals now refer to alcoholism as 'alcohol dependence syndrome' and distinguish between mild, moderate and severe dependence (see page 6).

Though not classified in this country as an illness, alcoholism is a dependent condition whereby the taking or not taking of the next drink goes far beyond the will. Without a spiritual insight, the dependent person cannot say no. That insight can usually only be found inside self-help organisations and treatment centres which in simple and direct ways address the emotional, physical and spiritual aspects of the dependent person.

Anyone who consumes alcohol may experience alcohol-related problems. Normally these would have a 'sobering' affect – one would not want to repeat them – but when and if problems persist (as in the case of someone becoming dependent) the person may then be termed a 'problem drinker'. It is likely that this person will have come from the ranks of the heavy social drinker.

Problem drinking is a term used to classify abnormal, usually excessive, drinking that leads to disturbances in social function and/or deterioration in health. A problem drinker becomes an 'alcoholic' when drinking becomes the most important aspect of his or her life. Everyone is affected by problem drinkers: individuals, family members and society as a whole. The excessive drinker (who may progress to chronic alcoholism) is considered different from the alcoholic in that he or she is able to stop drinking if given sufficient good reason for doing so, whereas the victim of chronic alcoholism cannot voluntarily abstain for more than a short time.

Dr Brian Wells, consultant psychiatrist and honorary director of the Centre for Research on Drugs and Health Behaviour, and who runs SHARP, says that for basic treatment purposes he accepts the definition that *an alcoholic is a man or woman whose life is controlled by alcohol*. Similarly, a 'drug addict' is someone who is wholly preoccupied by their chosen drug.

Alcohol Dependence Syndrome – a new theme

In the 1970s an innovation in alcohol studies produced a new way of describing the condition, now known as Alcohol Dependence Syndrome. This does not try to imply a cause of the condition, but rather pieces together symptoms which, taken as a whole, indicate that a person has a drink problem.

Alcohol Dependence Syndrome (ADS) is replacing alcoholism in the professional terminology and is considered a more attractive, apt, and subtle description in medical circles. It is not very common now to find a worker in the alcohol field employing the word 'alcoholic'.

The ADS has seven key features, all of which need to be present to enable the syndrome to be recognised:

- The drinker 'narrows' the choice of places where drink is consumed because the drink is now more important than the environment or the company.
- Alcohol becomes important to the drinker. He or she may change jobs to get closer to drink and neglect other aspects of domestic life or work.
- Tolerance to alcohol will change. Consumption increases to obtain the desired effect. As the central nervous system adapts to the effect of the drug, some get enormous tolerance, for instance the 30 pints on Friday night man. In others tolerance can be lost and only a few units will render them drunk.
- As the alcohol level in the blood drops, repeated withdrawal symptoms develop – shakes, sickness, sweating, anxiety. Hangovers are a mixture of all of these combined with dehydration and chemical imbalances.
- The drinker will consume more to relieve the symptoms, raising his blood alcohol level.
- A compulsion to drink takes over. Non-alcoholic beverages are not a substitute. A threat to deprive can result in anger and everyday life is disturbed.
- If, after a period of abstinence, the drinker starts to drink again, he or she will return to dependent drinking, even after 20 years or more of not drinking. The drinker will experience withdrawal and all of the other features of the ADS. The more dependent the drinker, the quicker the old problems are reinstated.

There is no doubt that some people will progress to dependent drinking, come what may. Some recovering drinkers describe themselves before drinking their first alcoholic beverage as having been 'alcoholics waiting for a drink'. Soon after their first drink they were drinking compulsively for the effect. Research now indicates a genetic factor in dependent drinking. It is complicated research and far from complete, but work already done suggests that people with a family history of alcoholism are four times more likely to develop dependent drinking patterns. However, medical opinion varies and a body of it suggests the more potent influence is society's inexpensive, available and enticingly varied drinks served in increasingly alluring environments.

The unit system and sensible drinking limits

As a first step in educating people on sensible drinking, the Health Education Authority established a unit system for measuring 'sensible' levels and otherwise.

A Unit is defined as:
- half a pint of ordinary beer, lager or cider (strong beers contain more units. Special Brew is 4 units)
- a single measure of spirits
- a standard glass of wine
- a small glass of sherry
- a measure of vermouth or aperitif

There are no *safe* limits, but the HEA recommends that sensible limits are:

- 21 units per week for men
- 14 units per week for women

The HEA says that too much for good health would be:

- 36 units or more a week for men
- 22 units or more a week for women

Danger limits are:
- 50 units or more a week for men
- 36 units or more a week for women

The Health Education Authority says it is rare for anyone drinking as much as this not to be harming themselves. (And remember most home-poured drinks are more than one unit.)

Women are more at risk than men from the harmful affects of alcohol because of the lower water content in their bodies. In men, between 55 and 65 per cent of body weight is water. In women the figure is between 45 and 55 per cent. Alcohol is distributed through body fluids so in men the alcohol is more diluted. Drinking alcohol is not recommended for women who are pregnant or who are planning pregnancy. However, one unit once or twice a week is not considered likely to be harmful to the foetus or to a baby whilst being breast-fed.

How alcohol affects your body

Alcohol is absorbed from the stomach into the blood within twenty minutes of ingestion. It circulates around the body to each organ; thus all parts of the body are susceptible to the direct toxic effects of alcohol.

There is enormous individual variation in susceptibility to harm but in general the greater the intake, the greater the likelihood of harm.

The time of onset of the condition varies greatly from individual to individual. Some people have severe symptoms after 2-3 years of heavy drinking while others have mild symptoms after 20 years. What is common to everyone is the time taken by the liver to eliminate alcohol. This can only be achieved at one unit per hour.

The use of alcohol to excess is associated with a huge range of illnesses, including heart disease, strokes, throat cancer, kidney damage, hepatitis, and loss of libido.

The *Observer* newspaper columnist Dr John Collee has said of alcohol: 'It causes a panorama of medical, psychological and social problems that makes Hogarth's Gin Lane look like Britain's best-kept village.'

Dispelling the myths

There are many myths concerning alcohol; we can demolish a few:

- Beer is not weaker than spirits. There are ingredients in beer that make absorption and hence drunkenness slower than in spirits, but the important factor is the amount of alcohol consumed, not its form.
- Alcohol is not a stimulant. The initial effects of drinking are mild relaxation and elation, but this is due to alcohol's depressant effect on the brain.
- Alcohol does not warm you up. Alcohol raises the pulse and blood pressure causing a misleading feeling of warmth. In fact, alcohol causes the body to lose heat.
- Drinking black coffee, having a cold shower or getting fresh air do not help sober you up. The only thing that does this is time – the elimination by the liver of one unit of alcohol per hour, waking or sleeping.

- Alcohol contains a lot of calories but there is no nutritional value in them. Excess alcohol can stop the body from absorbing vitamins.

Government action

In the 1980s, information on alcohol and its joys and woes received more enlightened attention than ever before. Dependent drinkers started to come out of the closet. Organisations were set up to address the issues.

In Britain, Alcohol Concern was established in 1984 as a national charity, with central government funding, with the following stated aims:

- to reduce alcohol-related harm and to represent those working to this end
- to raise public awareness of the risks of alcohol abuse
- to inform and educate people about the recommended limits for drinking
- to support and improve services for people with drink problems
- to improve action, locally and nationally, to prevent the harm caused by excessive drinking.

The Government set up a committee of ministers and reports have followed. However, Mark Bennett, editor of Alcohol Concern's magazine, reports that although there is now a high level forum in which alcohol issues can be raised, it is clear that the Government still has no overall strategy for reducing the harm arising from the misuse of alcohol. He calls for:

- automatic indexation of alcohol excise duties
- more money to be spent on alcohol education to counter seductive and misleading alcohol advertising
- banning inappropriate sports sponsorship, such as that of motor and water sports
- mandatory 'unit' labelling of all drinks (bottles, cans and other containers)
- the introduction by the police of random breath tests
- clarification of funding arrangements for residential alcohol services after the introduction of community care in April 1993.

Denial – the life-blood of addiction

Denial is the life-blood of addiction. It permeates all aspects of the problem and contradicts what is really happening, thus perpetuating the illness. By refusing to accept what is happening, the dependent drinker does not have to face reality and can subconsciously *deny* the consequences. The interviews in Part Two illustrate how this denial has to be faced before recovery can begin.

The guilt and shame can be so painful that either he will not talk about his drinking or he will deny it is causing any problems. In either case, he *defends* his dependence. The blame can lie elsewhere. He is absolved.

Dependent drinkers will conceal the amount they are drinking. They believe they do not drink more than 'normal' people while in reality they are drinking much more than the social norm.

People close to the dependent (the codependents) who deny what is happening are instinctively trying to protect themselves from the pain and loss in their lives. Full of anxiety, they do everything they can to tidy things back into place, to make believe the situation is other than what it actually is. They minimise the value of what they have lost, refuse to accept the evidence of their emotions, deny their own feelings, adopt a 'don't care' stance.

In times of great stress, those around addicts shut down their awareness of things that distress them too much, in order to be able to cope. This can serve to protect the codependent until he or she acquires the resources to deal with their real feelings about what has happened. At that point, for those facing reality, the experience can be devastating.

The pain felt at the loss of denial can be as difficult to bear as the grief felt at the loss of a loved one.

At times like these, the codependent should seek support from others who have faced similar trauma either through self-help groups or counselling. It is also advisable to seek professional help by opening up to your family doctor. See page 16 for more information on codependency.

The addictive personality can certainly be harnessed to make a good recovery, and such is the tenacity of that personality to pursue its ends, that a recovering addict is a force to be reckoned with, hence the positive energy felt in meetings attended by recoverers – newcomers and old hands alike.

It is of enormous help to many of us to know that an alcoholic is seen as a sick person needing to be well, not a bad person needing to be good. We alcoholics do such bad things that it is good to be told that it is an illness.

The power of denial is such that *outside* the mode of recovery, most people don't want to acknowledge the problem. It's just too much to deal with. However, the power of one alcoholic to share and identify with another's experiences is what most helps people to discover that they're not alone.

Inside recovery, in fellowships and treatment centres, it's wonderful to find that there is a willingness to own up to one's insanity. As one actor told Anthony Hopkins: 'You ought to hang around this fellowship Tony, because you'll get crazy like the rest of us, but you'll get better and you don't have to drink.' He meant that inside the fellowship, with everyone expressing exactly how they feel, one hears the great universal cry of pain expressed. Once that pain has been expressed and shared, it becomes much easier to bear. So consider this – for just the price of a phone call, you can tap into the power, strength and support of a fellowship such as Alcoholics Anonymous.

Alcoholics Anonymous

Alcoholics Anonymous (AA) started in Akron, Ohio, on 10th June 1935 as a result of the efforts of two alcoholic men. One was Bill Wilson, a stockbroker, the other Bob Smith, a doctor. By pooling their experience, strength and hope they managed to sustain each other's, and thereby their own, sobriety. Each had been a hopeless drunk and in their attempts to get sober, they had tried every method other than 'sharing' their experiences.

After achieving sobriety, neither drank again. They stayed sober by accepting that their lives had become unmanageable and that they were powerless over alcohol. They realised too that their recovery would be secure if they didn't take the next drink. Soon, in the anonymity of their new fellowship, they were known as 'Bill W' and 'Dr Bob'. Both are now dead but still embody the core-strength of AA. They were men of remarkable though differing qualities, and complemented each other. Bill W. was sober a year before Dr Bob. Of the two, he was the one with the higher profile, though when attempts were made to thrust fame on him he rejected it and would not permit his name and likeness to be published. He was described by Aldous Huxley as the greatest social architect of the century.

There are now tens of thousands of meetings throughout the world, in every continent, pole to pole. In Britain there are more than 2,600 AA groups. Many groups meet weekly. In London and the big cities there are meetings every day, some in the morning, some at lunchtime, some in the evening. The total for London exceeds 300.

Wherever you live in Britain there is a meeting within reach and a member willing to get you there. The only requirement for membership is a desire to stop drinking. No one questions you, checks you out, signs you in. There are countless people arriving drunk as they walk through the door.

AA is not a crusading organisation, nor is it a temperance society. The successful members are people who in the past have been unable to control their drinking but who now can by staying away from a drink one day at a time. It is never too late nor too soon to start. In the small market town where we live there are two meetings where 20 years ago there were none, and there are members in their twenties and in their eighties.

AA meetings are enormous fun because some of the most interesting people you ever met or dreaded meeting, or avoided in bars, or watched from behind the sofa when they came on chat shows drunk, or loved or hated to read about, may be found in these rooms, sober, unquarrelsome, happy and content, sharing their terrible stories and their joy in recovery. The AA rooms are not full of moralists who frown on drink.

AA is now an established, growing force in the world. More than a million lives have been saved and many millions more have been made joyful by the recovery of loved ones.

The AA book, known as the 'Big Book', contains the principles of the recovery programme. It is now in its forty second printing and third edition. Four million copies have been printed and distributed. It cost about the same as a half bottle of whisky.

For all that it was written more than fifty years ago when much less was known about the illness, its words ring true to every alcoholic. It lists the various methods familiar to every alcoholic who has tried to control their drinking.

Bill W. was so certain of the power of the programme of recovery that he and his fellow pioneers had set down, that he wrote in the fellowship's book: 'Rarely have we seen a person fail who has thoroughly followed our path.'

The Twelve Step Programme

When he was setting up AA, Bill W. created the twelve steps which form the basis of recovery, writing the first draft in just half an hour while lying down recovering from an illness. The Twelve Steps suggest a stage by stage progression for the fellowship rooted in an admission of powerlessness over alcohol and a willingness to change. These steps, or priorities, identify the need for relinquishing self will in exchange for a belief in a benevolent power greater than the self and for rigorous examination of that self. These steps should ideally be used as guides in every aspect of daily life. In terms of one's interaction with others, the Twelve Steps highlight the importance of addressing our failings, making amends and helping others towards recovery. Bill knew the use of the word 'God' in the Steps would alarm non-believers so he added the phrase 'as we understand him' so that AA could continue to benefit from what he called 'the great contribution of our atheists and agnostics.'

No one who is in a fellowship of recovering alcoholics need fear failure or recrimination. Everyone in the meeting rooms where alcoholics gather has admitted their powerlessness over alcohol and has agreed that their lives became unmanageable. The wonder of the twelve-step programmes is that whenever anyone returns, beaten again, there is a welcome, a cup of something hot and a nest of safety as long as the alcoholic needs it.

No alcoholic need ever fear being alone.

Indeed you need never fear anything because, as shown in the interviews in Part Two, fellowships for recovering alcoholics and addicts follow programmes which are not only for giving up drink and drugs without feeling a void, but also programmes for living in the real world, with all its difficulties, debts, disappointments and broken dreams.

If everyone was 'in' or 'on' some sort of programme of recovery, the world would be an infinitely better place and from the stories of recovery from active alcoholism in this book, you will see there is much more to gain than simply being able to stop drinking or drugging. People have started living a far better life with more fun and satisfaction, and infinitely greater sensitivity to their surroundings and to people close to them.

The *principles* of Alcoholics Anonymous have been a primary source of recovery for almost all of the men and women interviewed in Part Two, though this is not to say that they are necessarily members of Alcoholics Anonymous since anonymity is a source of the strength of the AA fellowship.

The Twelve Traditions of AA provide a pattern for the guidance of Twelve Step groups; they guard the unity and integrity of the fellowship. Even now, nearly sixty years after the founding of the movement, members are guided by the eleventh of the Twelve Traditions of AA to remember that 'Our public relations policy is based on attraction rather than promotion; we need always maintain personal anonymity at the level of press, radio and films.'

And books? Some people will prefer to be guided by the tradition. Others, acknowledging that AA has been *their* saving and, with our more open society enabling greater frankness in public life than in the 1930s, say they are members of AA, admit that it has been the makings of them, and feel that they may as well use mass communication to pass on their good news.

AA was never a secret society nor an authoritarian one.

Others, and this has been the greater tendency in the interviews, acknowledge freely that they have achieved sobriety one day at a time through the Twelve Steps *which have their roots* in the AA programme, and then leave it at that. In these cases the Tradition is thereby undisturbed. This is a healthy personal choice and in accordance with AA's guidance.

Where AA *is* specifically credited with recovery it is, equally, considered that the fellowship is powerful enough to withstand personal declarations of membership. No one is claiming spiritual perfection nor permanent sobriety. We maintain our condition one day at a time.

No one in any case speaks for AA or Al Anon (the codependents' fellowship) as a whole, and we, Derek and Joan, speaking for ourselves have decided that we might as well 'out' ourselves and trust the higher power to see us through.

Cross-addiction

Cross-addictions are widespread in the field of alcohol-dependency. Anyone suffering from an addictive personality could find themselves susceptible to one or more of the following:

- a snort of cocaine to counter the effects of drink (sometimes known as 'straightening you out')
- nicotine, deadly and legal
- amphetamines (speed) to supply 'energy'

- tranquillisers to calm you down
- heroin (some people's 'perfect drug'; hell for many and hellishly expensive; and because it's illegal and a heavy drug of dependency, it is a massive cause of youth-crime)
- gambling
- over-eating
- and all the rest – shopping, sex, chocolates, television, people, places, things.

The addict, moving in and out of denial, has to overcome the contradiction between the wish to be well again and the urge to take the next drug. An addictive personality can legitimise any drug, any irrational decision. Few addicts have just one drug, but there is usually a drug of choice about which, in denial, a good deal of tosh will be talked by the user who is determined to defend it.

The compulsive gambler, trying to put right one chance strike that went wrong, will take another haphazard shot believing he or she can get the money back – *and more*.

A gambler will change from black to red after terrible losses on the black on the roulette wheel. Why should red win *now*? The punter at Kempton Park backs all one particular jockey's mounts in the first five races and *all* lose. To 'make a profit' on the day, he decides to put the £500 he has just borrowed on another jockey in the sixth race. The original jockey wins. Betrayal!

Cross-addicted people will sometimes believe that if they have given up the drug they *really* like (drink perhaps) then the others are more permissible. Self-deception is crucial and is a central factor in addictive behaviour. The addict convinces himself that what he is doing is actually doing him good.

Codependency

In the years since I, Derek, gave up, Joan never reproached me for the drinking days. It had often been great fun to pub-crawl together and we had some fabulous parties before things got really out of hand. Many of our friends were heavy social drinkers and a few were practising alcoholics. None were ever teetotallers.

In recent times, we have recreated our marriage to become remarkably better than the one it replaced and that it *is* so is evident to all of our family and friends. We are all enriched by the recovery. It is said that the lives of at least five other people are affected by the behaviour of each alcoholic, and many studies have been carried out on the alcoholic family – on the children, wives, husbands and parents of alcoholics. It can also affect the 'extended family' – friends, neighbours, employers, etc.

What is clear is that everyone within a relationship which is affected by compulsive drinking is reacting to an abnormal situation where self-pity, resentment, bewilderment, pessimism, euphoria and chaos chase each other around on a merry-go-round of denial. My, Joan's, own experience of this merry-go-round/madhouse will be recognisable to many people caught up in a compulsive drinker's life.

Some members of the family unwittingly encourage the illness, because they don't understand its true nature. They become enablers or caretakers, saving the alcoholic from the consequences of his or her behaviour. Friends and colleagues often see only the cheerful aspect of the drinking – the fun and laughter in the pub. They don't see the violent scenes and arguments which may follow when the alcoholic arrives home.

However badly the alcoholic behaves, there is usually someone around to help diffuse the crisis. And so the alcoholic is rescued again and again from painful consequences, most often by his nearest and dearest. A partner will take on many additional roles to compensate for all that is being neglected within the relationship. As the alcoholic becomes more and more dependent on others, he goes on believing himself to be a free spirit. A mad paradox – one of many.

While this dependency increases, so too does the denial. Guilt is passed around as everyone involved looks for reasons behind the upsets. There is shame and loss of trust. Behaviour patterns develop which make the illness worse. Between incidents, the spouse will go into denial, unable to face either the alcoholism or the other problems within their relationship. The alcoholic denies there are any problems, and if there are, he believes that they are most probably caused by the family making a fuss.

The word codependent entered the vernacular of the world of recovery in the early 1970s to define in general terms a person whose life was adversely affected by someone who was alcoholic or chemical-dependent.

Codependents are people who allow other people's behaviour to affect their own behaviour to such an extent that they become totally preoccupied with trying to manipulate and control the way others behave. Codependents allow their own well-being to be hooked into the condition of the person who is alcohol- or chemical-dependent and, since the latter are sick people, the codependent cannot become other than sick too.

Codependents are essentially people who *react* to the problems and actions of other people close to them, and to their own problems. Rarely do they *act* with simple assertiveness, independence, detachment or in a constructive way. The battle for codependents is to learn fresh and beneficial ways of coping and to learn to take responsibility for oneself first.

Learning to act in healthy ways is the purpose of the Al-Anon family groups which were originally formed in the 1940s for the relatives and friends of alcoholics. Whether their alcoholic is in recovery or not, by coming together they can find better ways to solve their common problems. They use the Twelve Steps adapted from the AA programme. There are currently 472 groups in the UK.

What can codependents do for their own recovery?

At first it was difficult for me, Joan, to accept the concept of alcoholism as a sickness. It isn't easy to see that compulsive heavy drinking is not a deliberate and wilful act. And so we codependents shout, argue, cajole, or try to manipulate the alcoholic into more appropriate behaviour. Then we suffer the despair of failure. Nothing changes, yet we *must* change.

Although changes *are* hard to make, it is more creative – and ultimately rewarding – to endure the struggle of changing ourselves than to suffer, passively, the pain of our old responses and behaviour patterns.

If the intolerable situations we face seem immovable, then it is we who must take action to deal with ourselves. It is best to get on with our own lives and adopt a non-rescuing approach to the alcoholic. We *can* learn to detach ourselves from the alcoholic behaviour, and take more time caring for ourselves and our own responsibilities. It can be very difficult – some of us may have promised to love, honour and obey in sickness and in health; and then what if it is our child who is involved. In all cases we still have to accept that there is nothing we can do to change their condition (goodness knows how many times we have tried and failed). What we can do is change our own response to it.

In the twelve step programme of recovery HOW stands for

honesty, openness and willingness. The first step is to acknowledge honestly how much of a problem the drinking has caused. The next step is to be open enough to seek help. Alone we have become too overwhelmed and baffled to know what to do. Talking to another person who understands our feelings will lessen the sense of isolation, and relieve stress.

There are community projects dealing with alcohol dependence set up around the country, and there is a healthy network of twelve step self-help groups who are as close as a phone call away. From the moment we make contact, our problems can become more tolerable. In time, with the help of a counsellor or a group of fellow-sufferers, we can find some peace and purpose in our life, and regain a sense of well-being. But *we* have to be willing to change.

By repressing such strong emotions as guilt, anger, despair, jealousy, hatred even, we can cause long-term damage to our health, physiologically as well as psychologically. Talking about our feelings in a trusted and safe environment can help to heal the wounds.

In our recovery we learn to take care of our *own* responsibilities and our health improves; we can set ourselves free from the obsession to control the alcoholic and his behaviour. Releasing the alcoholic to become responsible for his own actions can be the beginning of his process of recovery, too.

The joy of recovery

Alcoholism is cunning, baffling and powerful, but it is not irremediable. Help is right here. Almost anyone can get sober and love it. This disease of alcoholism – and it is a disease – though incurable, can be arrested permanently in the twinkling of an eye. By staying away from that next drink, only one day at a time, or if you prefer, one minute at a time, the problem is over.

Reading the stories which follow, you will discover how it was for the nineteen people who initially liked what drink did for them and what eventually happened to them, and how it is now in sobriety.

· PART TWO ·

The stories of recovering alcoholics and their codependents that follow disclose how life used to be before recovery, what happened and how it is now. Without exception, each story is, inevitably, one of victory – of coming out of the shadow into the sunlight, of getting sober and loving it.

· DEREK TAYLOR ·

$\diamond$

My own drinking story goes back to the late 1940s when, slightly shy and slightly ambitious, I worked on a local newspaper in the small seaside town where I had lived all my life. It was crucial that I mix freely with the locals, but I was sometimes insecure and nervous of the self-assurance of the Rotarians, Freemasons, sporting hearties, and apparently powerful worthies who ran the town. It was a great relief to find that, the very first time I drank it, alcohol made me feel more confident. Nothing had ever worked like that before.

In the early years, I was rationed by the purse. At first I drank only at weekends, strictly beer, and I made a lot of friends of all ages, felt more at home with girls, discovered the joys of pubs and liked pub people. I did well at work and progressed in the army during National Service, becoming a sergeant.

All the time my drinking was escalating, first to beer every day, then to spirits at weekends, and, in the army, to spirits every day. I established a much admired reputation as a heavy drinker and valued it greatly, treasuring it above all other 'values'. These were un-enlightened times. It suited me very well to become 'one of the lads' by drinking. It was so much easier and quicker than becoming good at any other recreation. I believe now that I was, always, an alcoholic waiting for that first drink. I took to it *so* fast.

From the earliest days I know how it wrecked me and – as with other alcoholics – it was that 'wrecking' that I enjoyed. The old, much-loved phrase 'Never again' in the depths of the Greatest Hangover Ever Known is so quickly replaced by a wonderful sense of renewal and wellbeing with the 'hair of the dog'. The shakes that were so bad at first light are all but gone as the new injection of alcohol gets to work and all the world seems friendly again, fine resolutions melt away, the doubters are silenced and your own intellect is put to bed. In my twenties, I started having what I now know as blackouts, but which were then 'can't remember a thing about last night, after ten o'clock . . .'.

After the army I enjoyed uninterrupted success in journalism, working my way up to become feature columnist on the Daily Express. By now, I was married to Joan and we had four children. I joined the Beatles as Press Officer, and drank and drugged my way through London to Hollywood, where I set up as a press agent on Sunset Boulevard, with mighty sixties pop stars on my books.

After a while I rejoined the Beatles. By this stage I was taking loads of LSD, pills, coke, pot and poppers, and drinking all day and all night, moving up into the higher reaches of the record business and producing successful albums. We now had six children and now I really lost touch with my marriage and misplaced all sense of reason. I was pouring whisky, brandy, gin, beer and wine in to my body non-stop.

At the beginning of 1973 I was taken for a walk whilst in the depths of a vile hangover after a ten-day Hogmanay bender. On the walk, my friend Jonathan suggested I *might* be an alcoholic. After all, I did seem to have a problem stopping drinking when I'd 'had enough'. I thought about it seriously as we walked and then agreed, I *did* have a problem with drink but I was not, I thought, *alcoholic*. That was far too extreme a word. However, I decided I would stop.

So, that January I did stop and then I started again and cut down and cut back and then occasionally broke out on sprees and benders. For all that year, I was in and out of cutting down, back, out and back in again, doing all those things Bill W. talked about in the book Alcoholics Anonymous – '. . . never drinking alone, drinking only beer, etc'. I moved from periodic contentment and self-congratulation to black-out and wild remorse.

Finally, after one night of abusing everyone once too often with relentless resentment and sarcasm, and extravagant physical falling about, into the river, on the stairs, into bed, I was called to account by Joan and – for once – all six children (aged from six upwards, all loyal both to me and the larger family) who asked that I please acknowledge that I was indeed powerless over alcohol and that my life had became unmanageable. Would I please, at last, phone someone who was able to discuss alcoholism.

It was a Saturday morning. I said I would certainly go without drinking that weekend and would phone someone on Monday. 'Now', they all said, 'You must do it now.' So I did. I phoned AA, as I had heard it was a fellowship that dealt with alcoholics who were prepared to seek help. Immediately help was at hand. First they told me that my call was by no means unusual, particularly after a 'heavy

Friday night'. I immediately recognised that was what I'd had. How many heavy Fridays had there been? Maybe 1,250 since I had first started drinking, rarely a dry Friday since Attlee was prime minister.

The fellowship arranged for a local person to telephone me to re-assure me that none of what had happened was unusual. There were a lot of people who couldn't handle alcohol. It wasn't a crime, take it easy. Don't have an alcoholic drink for the moment. Have a cup of tea or coffee.

Later that Saturday someone called at the house, and cheerily told me his own amazing story. He was a clear-eyed, apple-cheeked, white-haired old chap from the upper middle-classes who peopled that part of stockbroker country, the sort of chap who looked as though he had a sherry before lunch and maybe a whisky and water in the evening. He launched into such an astonishing tale of his own drinking history – the most appalling benders, falling in ditches and peeing in his pants, cursing railway guards and sleeping through his station night after night on the way home from Waterloo, hearing that cry dreaded by so many drunken, dead-to-the-world commuters: 'Portsmouth Harbour, all change'.

It was all over now, he said, as long as he didn't take that next drink, one day at a time, and for a great number of one-days-at-a-time now, he had *not* taken that next drink. What did I think I would like to do next? Would I like to go to a meeting of the fellowship on Mon-day, two days away? I said I would and I said I wouldn't take the next drink and, one day at a time, I haven't, not since Ted Heath was leader of the Tory party.

I went to the meeting with another chap who looked as if he'd been a pillar of rectitude all of his life but who indeed had not. Now he was sober, happy and revitalised. At the meeting I fell in with about two dozen happy and healthy-looking people, most of whom spoke during the meeting, declaring 'My name is . . . and I am an alcoholic', following it up by saying how good they felt, and how hard their drinking days had become until they stopped. A lot of it passed in a blur because I was feeling very shaky. I managed to get out that my name was Derek and that I was an alcoholic. I didn't speak further that first night, but I haven't drunk since leaving that meeting.

I think that at first my dream in recovery was that I would cool things and then return to 'social drinking', but the more meetings I went to, the more I heard people talk about 'going back out there' and about the trouble they had got into when they'd decided to 'try a lager' or had 'a glass of wine on a plane'. Drinking had always ensued with renewed fury, sooner or later and somehow as the months passed it became a badge of honour with me that I really didn't want to go back to meetings and say I'd failed.

There *is* such a thing as social drinking, though I have enough insight into my own problem to know that I can't wander casually back into that wonderful rosey glow as if nothing has ever happened. There are, in any case, so many fabulous personal and family benefits from my sobriety that a couple of beers seem small beer indeed. And anyway, a *couple* of anything were no use to me, not from 1950 onwards. The first two drinks demanded company and they were rarely denied a party.

It wasn't easy in the outside world to expose one's 'insanities', though few of us, whether alcoholic or not, can get through life without experiencing crazy thoughts. Like many alcoholics I have had a tendency to grandiose plans, euphoria, irrational anger, a desire to procrastinate, an inclination to allow anxieties or fear to overwhelm me. I have, too, a desire to please. There is also a powerful wish to escape, to run from trouble, a feeling that I would like to blot it all out. All this is 'normal' in what is sometimes called 'alcoholic thinking'. Even in recovery, such thoughts can and probably will recur.

Inside the fellowships you will always find someone who will identify with you. In a way, and this may seem perverse, we cherish our bond of alcoholic thinking. It enables us all to relate to each other in recovery. You don't get into recovery unless you need to, and only by staying in the fellowship have I been able to find ways of dealing with alcoholic thinking.

I realised after many years of not drinking that the damage done to our domestic relationship had never really been addressed. I had stopped drinking, life had almost immediately got a whole lot better and we had left it at that. It is only in the past three years or so that Joan and I have dealt with the insecurities within our relationship and 're-started' our marriage in the mode in which we would have liked to pursue it all those years ago.

We caught up. We were not too late. We *hadn't* divorced. So, messianic or not, we have something here that has proved that it is never too late to begin again. Sobriety, whenever it is begun, is the commencement of growth. Heavy drinking is an automatic brake on maturity. Active alcoholism or compulsive drinking and growth are incompatible. They *cannot* co-exist. The rages, tantrums, alibis, excuses, remorse, cajoleries, physical debilitation, absenteeism, time-wasting, squandering of relationships, anger, intolerance, self-pitying, resentments and betrayals of trust that accompany the person who *must* drink are the opposite of adult behaviour.

One day at a time, the years have slipped away and, although there have been countless other problems in life, I have remained sober. My name is still Derek, I am still an alcoholic, but I no longer want a drink.

· JOAN TAYLOR ·

◇

My own story fits a predictable codependent's pattern. When I was seventeen I fell in love, at first sight, with the man who became my husband. In the early years of our relationship, it was fun to be around him. He was sometimes unreliable and I didn't like it much when he got drunk, but that didn't often happen when he was with me. He was full of good-humoured energy and I enjoyed going to pubs and parties with him.

We married when I was twenty and our first child was born a year later; as more children came along going out together wasn't very easy. Sometimes he went out and I stayed at home, but that seemed the natural order of things in the north of England in the early 1960s. Eventually we found good baby-sitters. After I put the children to bed, I would often catch a bus into Manchester and meet my husband in the pub near his newspaper office. I enjoyed the company and would drink halves of bitter with his colleagues, it was fun. We returned home by cab as neither of us drove a car then.

He developed into a 'big drinker'. This caused arguments and resentments between us as his behaviour became more and more unreliable. We began what was to become a pattern. After each upset we would try and bury our differences and get back to a loving relationship. I hoped that things would be different, but I had no idea how to set about making them so.

I remember one particular night, after I had put our three small children to bed and was preparing dinner, he arrived home drunk. As soon as I opened the front door he saw the disappointment on my face. In a typical pre-emptive strike he accused me of *causing* his condition – this was characteristic, 'classic' alcoholic behaviour. I was to be accused of being the cause of his drunkenness many, many times in the future. Although I knew then that his condition *couldn't* be my fault, later in the madness and unmanagability of the illness, I wondered if I *was* actually the cause. And so it went on, round and round, with nothing ever resolved.

I was baffled by his behaviour. I asked myself over and over, how *could* he be drunk again? I had absolutely no understanding of dependent drinking. I could only imagine that he wanted to be out and about and not come home until he was ready, and by then he would be drunk once more.

From my own family background I had come to believe that alcohol played an important part in 'having a good time'. I was not at all aware of the attendant *dependent* problems.

The years passed; we lived in Hampstead, California and Berkshire. There were lovely times, but the drinking confused us both; and in the confusion we lost our precious intimacy and trust. Our closeness was eroded by alcoholic thinking. I became frightened, nervous and full of denial, but I hung on hoping something would change. I couldn't leave and deny the children the loving relationship they had with their father, and he certainly couldn't support two homes. I was uptight and hurt and we weren't able to talk about the damage that was being done to our marriage without it ending in a row. I became short-tempered with the children; there were six by now. I needed the fellowship of other sufferers to help me come to terms with the wreckage of my emotional life, but it took me many years to find my way into a fellowship which helped the families and friends of addicts.

Before that, I had watched my husband go into recovery. Miraculously it was so simple at the end. He arrived home drunk while I was giving a dinner party for two of the children's teachers. He behaved badly and there was nothing I could do to cover up for him. The next day, our eldest child gathered all the others together, even the little ones, and they told their father that he must stop getting drunk. The game was up. There and then he faced the reality of his uncontrollable drinking and got in touch with a fellowship of recovering alcoholics. From the first days of recovery, he and I tried to be courteous and considerate with each other. Gradually I began to trust him again, and I admired him for his achievements in sobriety. But there was a lot of pain between us. It lay under the surface of my consciousness.

As our children grew older, not all of them missed out on the complications of dependency. My husband was a willing and selfless support, but by this time I was an exhausted wreck. We found a family self-help group and discovered that, at that time, there was nowhere else to go to get help. Together we learned about the importance of detachment and how to get on with our own lives. We learned the need to let go, but to go on loving. We supported each other by staying close to the programme. All the children are now well.

I visited a treatment centre run by Clouds House in Warminster where they were running family therapy groups. There I began to understand the nature of addictive illness, with its components of mental, physical and spiritual disease. I tried to find out as much as I could about it. I thought I was doing very well in my own recovery, but fourteen years after my husband attended his first meeting, I had a breakdown.

All the pain of the drinking years and the strain of the children's problems had been buried and now came to the surface and seemed to explode. Then I really needed the Fellowship and the support of kindly National Health Service GPs and psychiatrists, a stay in hospital (all NHS), friends and my family to help me get through.

It took two years to recover from the breakdown which was diagnosed as post traumatic stress disorder. Best of all, I discovered through it all, in my husband's sobriety, the enduring love and trust and intimacy I had thought would never be.

· BILL ·

Bill is a computer salesman from East Anglia.

I discovered alcohol at a very early age. My father was a hard-working coal miner, as was his father before him. Their recreation after a day down the pit was a few pints of beer in the local working men's club. At the age of 12-13 I started drinking. It seemed the most natural thing for me to do!

As a youngster I always felt left out of the crowd. I had no real friends. I would play with a lad who lived nearby who suffered from Downs Syndrome or any boy who was an odd ball like myself. I often enjoyed being by myself and although I joined all the usual boys clubs, Scouts, Boys' Brigade and Army Cadets, I never stayed for long. I enjoyed the street and the excitement of a bottle of cider from the pub off-licence.

At sixteen I considered myself to be a hardened drinker and a typical hard man, although at the first sign of any bother I was off. My aspirations grew and I became restless with my home life. Arguments with my parents dominated my domestic life during that year so I joined the Army. I didn't know where I was heading with regard to my future life. On reflection, like most young people, I lived my life a day at a time and never considered tomorrow. I did reasonably well in the Army. I developed drive and enjoyed the praise from my superiors. The more praise I received, the larger my ego became.

I was posted overseas at the age of 20. Now that was a place of joy for a drinker. Work ceased usually at 1 pm, bars were open all day downtown and my pay was good. Put all of those in a pot, stir, and what came out was the foundation of a drinking pattern that would lead me to years of misery, the most awful degradation and the loss of me – the real me.

I met my wife whilst overseas. Her father was in the RAF and he was also a drunk! She was a lovely girl but the relationship was a difficult one. Looking back, I was very immature. On returning to the United Kingdom we began our family. Even after the birth of my first

child I didn't change my drinking habits. I thought it okay to go out
with my mates four or five nights a week and leave my young wife at
home with our new baby daughter. Two sons followed, but not
much changed. My marriage was rocky although I am only aware of
that in hindsight. I decided, without consulting my wife, that I would
leave the RAF and pack our bags and leave for Australia. Eventually
that is where we set up home.

During my time in Australia my drinking began in earnest. I hated
my job. My employer didn't value me enough and my envy of those
that had their big houses and yachts was overwhelming. My self pity
increased at the same rate as my family's unhappiness. I gave up my
'new start' in Australia and dragged my protesting wife and children
back to England.

Back in 'Blighty' I felt safe for some time. My drinking continued
but it was not out of control. I progressed and obtained better paid
employment. I started travelling abroad and discovered that my
apprehension at a new meeting could easily be overcome by a glass
of brandy – at eight in the morning. The more I earned, the more I
drank. I spent most of my time at the pub. I found time for near
strangers but not for my growing children or my lovely wife, who
tried her very best to maintain a 'normal' life for the children. Today,
due to her great effort, my three children are happy, well-adjusted
people, particularly my two sons. My daughter was the one child who
suffered most from my ill temper and intolerance. I was a dreadful
father and husband.

By my early 30's I began to visit doctors to attempt to find something to stop me feeling the way I did. I hated myself. I couldn't sleep
without a drink. I couldn't attend a social function without a drink. I
couldn't work, travel, sign a cheque without trembling, visit the doctor or dentist, or even attend my father's funeral without a drink. My
wife began to threaten me with divorce. I drank and took more
mind-altering pills as my answer to our problems. Never any money,
no holidays for the children, emptiness in our hearts. On two occasions I was taken to hospital very ill from drinking. I tried 'shrinks',
meditation, religion, biking and even more pills, but nothing
worked. I was going downhill rapidly, afraid to go to bed at night
because of the nightmares I would encounter, afraid of the living. My
wife, in deep despair, arranged for the courts to have me removed
from the family home. It was New Year. I was now really alone. This
wasn't pretend stuff – I didn't live with my family any more – they
had gone.

Three weeks later, in utter misery, I made contact with Alcoholics

Anonymous. I attended my first meeting. I had been drinking that day and felt worse than I had ever felt. I arrived at the meeting. I remember a cold room with a few ordinary looking men. I listened as best I could to them. I knew immediately I had come to the right place. That evening I discovered that my problem was booze. Not the bad job, not my wife who I felt didn't understand me, not the fact I had been born a miner's son or any other reason – just the booze. A few days later, still drinking, but in torment, I was admitted to the local hospital simply to 'dry out'. I stayed there for seven days. I left and went back to AA. I haven't had a drink since that time.

I am now a member of AA. It forms the main part of the new foundation of my life. It has helped me grow as a person and to forgive myself, as I hope my family will someday. I now love my wife and family with a love that I understand to be a true love, a love that is free of control, a love that allows them the freedom to grow and fulfil their own desires. I am also free, free from the shackles of fear, anxiety and the spiritual sickness that very nearly destroyed me.

Thank God for AA.

• ERIC CLAPTON •

◇

Eric Clapton is a rock musician. He lives in London and Surrey.

I think I was one of those alcoholics who was a drunk waiting for a drink. I have strong, very pleasant childhood memories of being outside pubs. My folks were often in the pubs enjoying a country drink. They weren't alcoholics but they liked a good time. And to me it was actually very powerful. I'll never know why.

It was the magic inside these places that I wanted to know about, so when I was 14 I 'became 16' in order to get in there. My first drink didn't seem at first sight to be alcoholic because everyone else seemed to be doing the same thing. We were all getting as drunk as we could at a very young age.

Shortly after having my first drink in a pub, aged 15 I went to the jazz festival at Beaulieu. I was very keen to hear the music and see live jazz. We camped in the woods outside the grounds of the stately home and at lunchtime went into town and got legless – paralytic, puking and carrying on drinking for hours. I passed out somewhere around three or four o'clock and woke up a day and a half later. Everyone else had gone, and so had my sleeping bag and just about all my money. I crapped and I puked and I was virtually like a newborn baby – completely helpless. I don't know what the hell had happened but I felt a hundred years old, and a complete wreck. I had to try and make it home and even now I don't remember what I said to my grandparents who were raising me. I must have begged the money to get a train, and I suppose it shook me up for a few days but it wasn't long before I was back at it.

I was also learning to play the guitar so it worked for me to go into a pub and play and get free drinks. I felt part of the scene. I bought my way into the hippie/beatnik thing by being an entertainer and a bit of a jester. This was in the very early sixties.

At some point the music took over and I actually started to get jobs, turning professional in an amateur way at the age of 17. I had to be fairly sober and I did actually ease up for a long time; for about six or

34

seven years I was mucking around but really taking my music very seriously and studying it. During that period of time, drugs came into the picture and they weren't so debilitating. You could take a black bomber and go the other way from booze; you could wake up to the 'nth degree, play all night and whizz along. And so maybe there was a bit of chemistry going on. I was mixing the booze with the uppers but mainly just smoking joints.

Not only was I lined up for a drink from the word 'go', but I also felt very different because of my circumstances. I was raised by my grandparents – there's a certain oddity attached to that at school and I felt different. When I'd found out that I'd been adopted, I actually became a very intentional rebel. I deliberately went wrong at school, deliberately avoided any kind of team exercise or sport, deliberately set out to be a loner and chose things to do which were isolated from the mainstream: the particular brand of music I liked was almost un-heard of in this country.

It was a place to hide. It fitted in very well with my disease. But thank God, it did have a very big hold on me in its own right. It is a gift for which I'm very grateful and it's helped me in respects where I can see other alcoholics have had problems in recovering without really having 'anywhere to go' or any way to express themselves. I had my guitar playing and that helped to keep me on the straight and narrow through my twenties until around 1967 when drugs and everything just took off. I got involved with musicians who were heavy users of everything. Scotch, heroin and cocaine, they were all on the menu daily. They were older than me. One used to advise me 'Never do this. You can put things up your nose, but never shoot it in your veins,' which I never actually did. But it wasn't along before I tried all the other things that he'd forbidden me to try – or I'd forbid-den myself. I got into all of them sooner or later, just out of sheer curiosity. It didn't seem to me that any one of these habits was caus-ing me much of a problem. I had no family to support, I was pretty irresponsible and always had been.

It was no great change of ways. It wasn't as if I was doing a nine to five job and not turning up for work. I wrote my own ticket. When I was with that band, whatever we did, we did together. I don't think we actually had to cancel shows, but we all were in the same boat. There weren't any reprimands. It was a little co-operative unit.

I did run into a situation with one band where a member was a real alcoholic (possibly my first contact with a real one) who was constantly being thrown out of the band in somewhere like Maccles-field. He would get psychotic on rum, take over the microphone when we were on stage and curse the audience. We thought it was hilarious. It wasn't of course, but it was part of the age.

It all started to get very intense for me when I bumped into my (ex)wife because of the complexity of the situation, the guilt, and the illicitness of it all. This led me into hard drug-taking. I was really out of things for about three years from about 1969 to 1972. I stopped working altogether. That had never happened before. I was dabbling a bit with alcohol but I was mainly snorting heroin, and that is a very isolationist drug.

I ended up with another girl and both of us were using. We'd go through hell – three days of cold turkey – and then she would do the run to London to buy more. In a way, I was happy. I loved it, really loved it. The only things that dropped away were sex, and going to the toilet. I don't know how I got by. I was constipated for years, but you can manage all those things because it's anything for a fix.

I never could really see that campaign about saying 'No to drugs' because it is the power of drugs that makes you feel so good. And if you have a tendency to be an alcoholic, the addictive tendency to go down that road, you'll go down that road no matter what they say.

I did recover because I was really cajoled by this young lady's father whom I respected immensely. He was a tremendously kind man and he gave us an ultimatum. I think he was prepared to turn us over to the law if we didn't stop because he could see his daughter's life wasting away. Their family had been beset by tragedy over the years and he didn't want to see this happen again. He wrote me a very strong letter and then took some action. We went to see a lady named Meg Patterson took me into her home and treated me for heroin withdrawal with the acupuncture method she had devised. The method was quite widely used for a little while and it did remove some of the unpleasantness of withdrawal. However, there was no mention of recovery from alcoholism in this programme, nor of any fellowship for narcotics recovery; no suggestion of aftercare. No mention, really, of the spiritual vacuum that results from the absence of drink and drugs.

And so when one's 'cured' as they say, one's out on the street. I went out and got drunk. I couldn't actually take on normal life without something of some kind. Had there been some alignment with a halfway house, I may have been on the road to recovery then and there. I went to Wales to recuperate with a member of this young lady's family. I worked on the farm but at the end of each day we went off and got drunk and so my alcoholism took off. It seemed fair enough, a drinking life up there on the farm, excusable to collapse into the juke box every night at half past ten and pass out and be driven home.

However, that's really when my disease moved into fifth gear. Previously when hooked on heroin I never went out. I was a ghastly shade of yellow, covered in spots and scabs, grossly overweight and evil-smelling. I didn't wash or take care of myself at all. In contrast, I now lived on a farm, drinking with other people who drank hard and worked hard and I was healthy. To all intents and purposes I was actually building muscles, getting a tan and breathing plenty of fresh air. I had a healthy appetite. At the end of the day, I drank.

It did seem to be a new code of living which worked, but I don't remember going a single day without a drink. And then at the weekends, when we weren't working, I'd go to the pub in the morning and drink all day. It was great.

My particular disease was very hard to accept when I came into the fellowship, because I loved drinking very much. I had never, ever considered that it caused me problems – even when it was killing me. I was psychotic, hospitalised with ulcers, having double vision, attempting suicide and having experiences of the worse kind of melancholy and depression. I never would blame the drink because drink had become my best friend. I didn't blame anything. I refused to accept that there was anything wrong so there was no-one *to* blame.

Denial was so huge that I refused to face up to what was wrong. My 'excuse' was 'I'm an artist and this is how we live'. A lot of my early days were spent studying great musicians, great painters, etc. I thought 'Well they all seem to have gone this way. Perfectly acceptable and actually quite desirable'. Great to read about and see on television but when it's happening to you, and it's out of your control – it's not something you can put on like a coat – and it's not a pose, it's not so funny.

Shortly after this, I bumped into the lady I'd fallen in love with and the relationship took off again. It had been a very clandestine thing before but now there was a definite split in her marriage. She seemed keen to leave home whereas before she'd been trying to maintain the marriage. We went off together and began a long, long party which went on for about seven years. We had great times, but the drink was always there and at some point it got completely out of control for me. She started putting on the brakes and started having meetings with her friends, my manager and other musicians, discussing what to do with me. She'd say 'I know *I'm* in trouble but I think I can get it under control. I don't think he can.'

It all came to a head with me trying to do an American tour on a diet of Veganin and brandy and collapsing after the eighth show with three ulcers, one of which was bleeding. At the hospital they said that I was dying, as I arrived in fact. I was very lucky. I think my Higher Power put me in the right place to be treated. I was hospitalised for three months and the doctors started talking to me about alcohol. They could get to it straight away over there, but my denial was magnificent. In my head I made them believe me. I was English and therefore our drinking habits were completely different. 'I drink pints of beer and it's very good for you. It's got all these things in it. It's good food. I like the occasional glass of wine and maybe a brandy in the evening.'

This tallied with this picture I had of myself, this romantic entrepreneurial man of the world, with the occasional going off the rails, to let off steam. And so they let me out of there, with me making promises about where I'll cut down – I'll have just a glass of Scotch in the evening, etc

I think that by that time I was well aware that something was terribly wrong. When something's wrong, and it's something you can't talk about to even your closest friend, then you really are in trouble. I came home to England after hospitalisation, got straight back into drinking and rapidly got acquainted with double vision. I wasn't working very hard and would drink to attain double vision. It became a gauge for me. That was my condition. If my vision went back to normal, that meant I had to get stuck in again. This went on for quite a long time and seemed normal to me, but if that isn't insanity I don't know what is.

Around the same time I started staying up late at night. I'd drink all day, with my wife as observer, but there was actually another level as well. When she was watching, I'd be drinking lager or Special Brew but when she was out of the room, I'd top that up from another bottle I kept under the couch. That was because I couldn't drink properly when anyone was around. I couldn't drink in pubs because it was too slow. I now needed this stuff and I hadn't really accepted that.

From then on it was a very fast decline. My liver went; my sanity had gone. I had shotguns and was practically toying with suicide. I'd load the gun after my wife had gone to bed, and would go into these really rapid melancholic declines. Towards the end, every time I picked up a glass it could mean death. I had full knowledge of that.

I didn't forsee any good outcome. It wasn't going to be good fun. I had to, had to, had to drink. I knew there would be a point where I would be on my own in the middle of the night and I'd be thinking about killing myself, every bloody night. And I knew that at the outset of every day when I would pick up the first drink. I wasn't a binge drinker, I was a non-stop drinker. At the height of it, towards the end, I was sleeping for maybe three hours and then getting up and drinking and then going back to sleep. I had drink by the bed. I had it everywhere.

I think that was about the time of my rock bottom. That spiritual awakening we talk about in the fellowship happened to me when I had a moment of clarity, when I decided that I should call someone up and ask them for help. I suppose this had been at the back of my mind for quite a while.

A lot of us, I think, carry on drinking knowing that we are going to ask for help sooner or later. But not today. We'll do it tomorrow. We'll ask someone for help. One more day. One more day like what? It was madness, it was a nightmare and I nearly died three times by my own hand.

I called up the most significant person to me, the person who, years ago, first indicated to me that there was a very clear problem when he said 'You know you've definitely got a drink problem and you're going to have to face it sooner or later.' Anyway, I called him and he said 'Pack a bag and just wait. Try and lay off the sauce. Just hang around for a few days. We'll sort something out'. He just came over one day, picked me up and we got on a plane to America. I went to Hazelden residential clinic which was 'very alcoholic' in a way because I had to be best, go straight to the source. They had a very good success rate. I didn't go there sober. I drank the plane dry. We stopped at every bar that one could see on the way to Hazelden. When I got in there they put me straight into detox for about three days; they put me on librium, to get me through the next three or four days and then I was in a treatment unit.

I was really shocked when they first started telling me 'Well, you know you can't drink. You won't be able to drink again, but don't think of it like that. Think of it as one day at a time.' I didn't grasp much of the programme, but I did do a lot of 'tap-dancing', trying to get through the thing with a smile on my face, which was not what they wanted. I was very dishonest. I did pick up some of the jargon, did go to all the lectures; I put part of myself into it but there was a voice in the back of my head saying 'Fuck all this, you can still do it'.

My self-will was very strong. I got my medallion and they let me go at the end of the month. They fixed me up with a connection in Surrey, *he* called *me* up – I didn't have to do a thing. I went with him to a meeting of the fellowship in Surrey.

So I started off on my voyage to recovery. The first couple of years in the fellowship in the early 1980s were very hard for me, because even when I was in treatment I was convinced at the back of my head that this was just a temporary phase. I was going to give this a try, but really drink was always going to be there. After about two years I quite disliked the people that I saw in the fellowship rooms, especially in my neck of the woods (there were brigadiers and tweed ladies) and there was a lot of what I saw as brainwashing and self-righteous rubbish. There were not many people of my age or sort that I could identify with and I looked for all the differences and none of the similarities.

I wasn't really aware of the problem of cross-addiction so I thought a lot about doing other things. I thought 'Well, maybe if I don't drink but have a joint or have a line of coke, that won't harm me. That isn't a slip.' There was a point where my marriage was very rocky and my wife still wanted to drink, wanted to go to parties and I found this very hard to cope with. I would go to a party and sit there with a coca cola and be very resentful about the whole situation. I started to devise a scenario in my head whereby I could maybe have the odd drink with her, we'd get back on an even keel with one another because we'd have something in common. And of course that was a rationalisation because what I really wanted to do was to go out and get blitzed, only I wasn't admitting it.

I had admitted to everybody in the rooms of the fellowship that I was an alcoholic. A lot of people have a problem saying that out loud. I found that very easy. But I hadn't really admitted it to myself. I was saying it but I was not accepting it. (Talking the talk but not walking the walk.) I was saying it but kept something back. Pretending to walk the walk, making a good job of it though. I think I pulled the wool over a lot of people's eyes because we alcoholics are very good at that. We have had years of experience.

One day I picked up a drink.

I picked it up in a pub on a summer's day, and it was just like a beer commercial. A lovely glistening pint of lager in a frosted glass and I thought 'Well this is what everyone would want.' I thought 'There's nothing wrong with this, at all.' I kept that up. For nearly three years. I couldn't go to a meeting. I knew morally I had no right to go to a meeting and throw aspersions on everybody else's sobriety by saying that I had had a drink today and it didn't appear to have done me any harm. I couldn't do that. So I stopped going to meetings, and without any kind of programme other than that which had instilled itself and with constant visits to pubs and glasses of wine with meals, a big-time slip was not far away.

Three years of that sort of controlled drinking was a long time but it was 'white-knuckle' and it was a nightmare because it wasn't what I wanted. It was for everybody else's benefit. One day after about three years had gone by, I bought a bottle of vodka and sat in my own little room where I used to watch TV and get blitzed. I drank the whole bottle of vodka in one sitting and got right back to where I was before, but worse really.

I went all the way down and I was back not just to the last days of my earlier drinking but much, much worse.

I wanted to go back to the fellowship rooms because I knew they could help. But I was scared to go back there because of this awful fear, and loneliness, because I felt as though I'd had a chance and I'd spat in their faces, and walked away from them. And I knew that the way I was now going was absolute, certain death. It was so accelerated, because my disease had gone so far that my tolerance had gone. One day I could drink two bottles, but the next day I could have one glass and I was all over the place. It was out of control.

I was limping around on stage, and I put the fear of death into the musicians who were with me; they really didn't know what was going on. My liver broke down. My skin was peeling off. I was covered in blotches. I was just a wreck. On the last tour of Japan, I sat in my room, drinking, getting room service. The band would take me out and try to walk me round the streets for a bit of air.

It was actually in Japan that I made up my mind that when I got back home I would go back in the fellowship, and that was a moment of clarity. I was a hardened drinker and I loved alcohol. I actually *loved* the taste of it, the smell of it, what it did for me.

People go on about families and relationships; I never had any. I'd been with a lot of people in my life and I didn't give a damn about any of them. I never did. The only thing I ever loved was alcohol. That was the only thing that never let me down. And when it did let me down, it was the biggest shock of my life. It broke my heart that I couldn't trust it any more. My friend had gone. And that was really what was happening to me in my first period of recovery. Though alcohol was what had ground me into the ground, I was not going to let it go. I wanted to give it another chance. You know, 'I owe this to my friend.'

So the next time I went into recovery, I went in with a will because now I wanted to stop drinking. I had given it its chance and it had done exactly the same – and worse – to me. I was broken in spirit really. My heart had been broken badly, and all kind of things had happened to me in this second period of drinking. I had left home and become involved with an Italian lady. She had got pregnant and had a child and that was one more reason for me looking at my drinking for the second time because suddenly there was a real responsibility in my life. I never considered my marriage a responsibility but this little baby somehow represented to me something really concrete in my life that I'd never experienced before, something that I was *always* going to be responsible for. Marriages can break up – a grown-up is a grown-up and can get by, but this little creature was my responsibility and I did feel a deep-seated feeling of belonging with this child. It helped me to have that moment of clarity and when I went into recovery, into treatment, back into Hazelden, I really got stuck in.

One of the first things I began to do was to pray. I have heard this around the rooms many times, that a lot of people are around the meetings for a long time without getting down on their knees and often, the first time you *do* get on your knees is when you start to get results.

For me, it's got nothing to do with belief or religion. It's a simple action and I don't even know if I believe what I'm saying half the time. It's like a conversation with something or with the air. Just the act of saying things brings them into reality because they're not in my head any more. They're actually out in the room and I can hear what I'm saying. Sometimes it shocks me to hear what I'm praying about.

When I did start praying in treatment, overnight I lost the compulsion to drink which had been with me since the age of fifteen, in one degree or another, the need to have something in my body that would alter my consciousness had always been there. That went away and in its place I had a desire to inter-relate with people and to learn about the programme. I actually had a desire to get better. I had never had that before. It was actually a swapping of bad habits for good habits; a desire to become good and better than I'd ever been. That was the miracle for me – to wake up and not have that worry, that fear of how am I going to speak to this person, how am I going to do that without a drink? It had all gone within the space of several days.

When I'd come back to England to take up normal life again, there was a whole new ballgame. I went to meetings – not as wholeheartedly as I do now, because recovery has been very slow for me and I find it difficult to take on board so many things at once. I have to do little things one at a time and try to keep it simple – but first of all I had a lot of the same thinking processes.

I really had to button my lip and listen. I went to the meetings and didn't say anything. The first time around I had been a big advocate of the fellowship; I went crusading, got self-righteous. This time round it wasn't like that.

I realised that I was at the beginning of something very important. It wasn't a game. It was life or death. I knew that everybody in those rooms was my lifeline. That realisation was a big step for me and accepting at last that I was an alcoholic was a fantastic relief. I've been taking it from there really. It's been four years and the first three years were really just plain sailing.

Until last year (the death of my son) I had had a very good recovery, a great recovery, a great sponsor, we got on like a house on fire, and still do. I found, suddenly, out of nowhere, thousands of people in the fellowship with whom I could now identify. I can't explain that other than the desire, the willingness to want to change, to get on. I started to attend meetings all round the world, wherever I was, and I started creating a space in my life for the programme.

Before, I'd not given this programme any room at all. Only when I was at meetings did I think about the programme. Now I tried practising it, tried to practise the Twelfth Step, to apply the principles of AA in all my affairs, just on a daily basis, the way I treated people, the way I handled my life. Now I asked if I could account for my life at the end of the day? Had I done the right thing?

I started to accept that a lot of things about me that I didn't like were probably always going to be like that. That that was just the way I am. I stopped beating up myself, stopped actually criticising myself. I started to become proud not only of myself and my successes as a musician but also of my recovery as well. My sponsor would always praise me and give me a big pat on the back. I still don't run myself down very much. I am quite happy.

In 1990 we were on tour in America. There was a helicopter crash and several of the group were killed. I suddenly found myself placed in the position of extreme responsibility because I was really the captain of this travelling ship. Now this ship does very well if there is no misfortune. It's a shared responsibility. Everyone carries their own weight and no-one is really the head of it. It just rolls along under its own steam. When the helicopter crash happened, I suddenly felt that everyone was looking at me to make a decision. We were nearly at the end of the tour with five more shows to do. There was a loss of direction; everyone was thrown right out of kilter. A lot of people wanted to go home. There was a strong feeling that we should pack up and get out of there. Go home, get out of America, didn't like America . . . you could blame it on all these things.

Now suddenly it was up to me to make this decision. I made a long distance phone call to the crew who were setting up in another town. With all of them in one room and all of the production crew in my room, we set up the phone link and spent three or four hours listening and talking and conducting ourselves as grown-ups, deciding the best thing to do. Mine was the swaying vote. I felt we should go on with the show because I thought it the best way to honour the relatives of those who had died. It got a unanimous vote, and we did go on with it. At any other time in my life I would have been a gibbering wreck in those circumstances. No-one would even have consulted me had I not been sober, because they wouldn't have wanted my opinion. I would have been drunk in a corner of the room. But at this point in my life they turned to me and asked me what they should do.

I'm immensely proud of that. I was immensely proud of it at the time. It gave me the evidence that my programme was working. In the fellowship we don't always know. It's very hard to gauge what kind of recovery you're making until you are in a crisis situation.In the following year my son was killed in an awful accident in New York.

I had spent about four years of our lives together, very haphazardly. Through talking to my sponsor it occurred to me that he was now coming to an age where it would be quite easy to communicate with him and I thought I should be making moves to organise a life together and deciding whether or not that would include his mother. How it would be arranged I didn't know, but it was going to be my aim that year to spend as much time with him as possible.

I cancelled all my working plans and the whole year was left vacant, after the Albert Hall concerts. I went off to New York to see him and while I was there, getting ready to go and pick him up for lunch, I got a call from his mother saying that he'd fallen from the window. She was hysterical and I immediately went into shock. I turned to stone. It was very odd. I immediately felt that I was going to be the one to take charge of the situation because I knew that my programme was going to click into gear. I actually knew it as I was speaking on the phone. I could feel this happening to me. 'I'm going to be sensible. I'm going to conduct myself in as dignified a way as possible. I'm going to take care of all the arrangement and I will be there for anybody who needs me.' I went through the whole thing with the police and the hospital, the undertaker and the family. I brought his body back here and went through the funeral without really flinching.

But what happened interestingly enough was that the minute I got back to my hotel in New York, from the scene of the accident, I got on to the fellowship. I called my temporary sponsor in New York and she got me to a meeting that night.

The word had got out about the accident. It was on the news and people knew what had happened. Not many people spoke to me but I could just feel this incredible love which I've never had anywhere else. Completely unconditional love, coming towards me. And it held me in place and made me able to do all the things I had to do. For the first time in my recovery I actually had a *use* for the fellowship.

Even in the three years of good recovery I had been running on my own will but now I was totally helpless. I called on people from my own group and I was asking and praying what to do. One bloke, Danny, who's one of my best friends in the fellowship, a lovely Scotsman, said to me 'If you don't start fucking sharing in this meeting, I'm going to clout you round the ear'. He was deadly serious. He meant violence. I replied 'Well, they always say better things than I do,' and he said, 'Well, in that case, just start the sharing. When the meetings open, you start and if you don't, I'm going to sort you out.' And that was it. I started sharing on a regular basis. I still do at every meeting I go to. I say something. I generally start the sharing and I have now started chairing the meetings.

I was happy in recovery, happy with my recovery but then the death, in sobriety, of my son, gave me something that I could give back. Just by virtue of the fact that I could sit at the head of the table in a meeting and say 'I haven't picked up a drink today and I didn't pick up a drink the day he died', I knew it was such a great message for those who were in doubt, who were having a hard time. It was my first chance to give something concrete back to the fellowship.

I had always been on the fringe; I had never been able to do tea or telephone service because I'm always on the road or travelling around. I don't have a regular lifestyle so service has been denied me. Now I recognised that service is a very integral part of the workings of the fellowship.

And that was the first time it all jelled. It was a horrible thing to happen but I can't say I wish it hadn't happened because that is life. It brought me into the rooms 100 per cent; I used the fellowship, and I listened to what I was told and I started to work the steps.

Step Three was very instrumental on a daily basis – being able to throw the whole mess into God's lap and say 'I can't deal with this.' I really started to doubt my own judgement then because when something like that happens, you realise that everything is so transitory that any kind of control you try to exercise over life is all purely an illusion.

I've had a lot of anger since the accident, that I've not really sorted out. And my programme has been shaky at times but I think that's to be understood. But I do live this programme as much as I can, a day at a time, and I go to more and more meetings and my sponsor says 'Now, it's time to take a fourth step – that is have a real look at yourself – because you've been getting very grouchy. Do a proper fourth step because the ones you did in treatment were really part of the exercise, part of the treatment.'

And this will be a very, very determined, constructive fourth step. I want to take a long time over it, and get on with life the way it is now.

I do feel like things are starting afresh for me. I've always wanted to be good at everything I do and one of the things I'm qualified to do is work a programme for recovering alcoholics. We are all qualified and it's there for us to work. I actually feel better if I'm going to a meeting each day. I feel that I belong with my own kind. I get satisfaction from that. And strength.

· JOHN CONTEH ·

◇

*John Conteh was boxing's light heavyweight world
champion and is now an entertainer and sports personality.*

There was always a dream, about the Big Time. I used to go to the
big parties, rock star parties with famous people in big flats in Belgravia. There would be loads of drink and they'd be chopping coke up
on the glass tables. The music would be playing and we'd all be
stoned.

This was the dream; this was the life. I wanted the money to get
that kind of life. I resented not being able to have that sort of house
and friends like those kinds of people. I thought it looked fantastic
and I couldn't see any other way of living. Boxing was just a way to
finance that. Being young and fit, I could just bomb back quickly by
just running and training.

What were we looking for? They say a lot of alkies are looking for
God. There is a scene in *Raiders of The Lost Ark* where the Nazis
open up the Ark and angelic creatures come out. They rise higher
and higher until they turn into monsters. Then they come roaring
right down and wipe out the Nazis completely. It was like that with
the drinking. The heights and the depths. The drinking clubs were
fine to start with but after a time I was looking round for good
people and didn't seem able to find them. They saw me coming.

I couldn't get into a lot of clubs, not in the end. At first I went to the
big clubs where everyone smiled at me. Then I moved downwards
and found myself in dives, shebeens, trying to look for friends and
some kind of relationship. That was hell because you knew you had
to wake up.

You'd taken the drink the night before; it had done its job which
subconsciously was to relieve the hell going on; even then you *know*
you're in hell. And you definitely are in hell ten hours later, rolling
around. Perhaps it's seven o'clock in the morning and you think
'Well I've got to go home now. It's daylight.' You've got to go to sleep
with the terror of it all.

Sometimes I used to go to a pub that was open for traders or such

47

like. You keep going there until you go to an afternoon place and then it was just like hell. You're whacked out. Notwithstanding all that, I'd still go on drinking because it seemed like I'd found the solution to the problems of life. I wanted to wipe out thoughts of people, places and things. And by taking a drink I *could* wipe them out and wipe out reality. The drink could give me the people, places and things *I* wanted.

Thank God, drink was there to relieve the hell I was going through. Or so I thought. What else was I going to do? Blow my brains out or blow somebody else's brains out? Not only did alcohol relieve the tension, unless I drank enough of it, I couldn't live Step One – I couldn't admit I was powerless over alcohol, that my life had become unmanageable.

Then I had one of those days; I woke up after about three hours' sleep with the terror. I had always tied up the music with drinks, clubs, discotheques – the dreamy state. It was five or six in the morning and I had a strong feeling about not liking people telling me what to do. (I still feel like that but it is just a case of accepting myself.) I asked myself: 'Why am I drunk? What's going to happen with my life?' In the middle of all that, right in the core, in the centre of my mind, I was able to ask those questions; a moment of clarity.

Given the state I was in, I thought that if I delayed I would drink again, and that's where I got an understanding of God, as I understood him. It was like magic, as if God was saying 'That's the only way I can help you. You've accepted you're powerless.' I had accepted. There was no defence.

There was no other way. My whole being had told me to drink. My whole life had been about drink. That was why my mental defence barrier had to be broken down. I was like a man with no legs as far as drinking was concerned. I still am. I have no defence. If I take a drink now, I won't just take one, I'll take hundreds. I'll drink right through, and I'll never stop.

My pattern was I'd drink hard, train hard, fight hard and drink hard again. Have a good booze-up then back in harness again. Then no drink. I'd deny myself everything to fight and get the money. It was a periodic thing.

When I finally faced up to what I was doing, I said to God (as I understand him) 'What should I do?' He looked at me and smiled. It was the first time I had been honest, got into the depth of honesty, in the midst of all that fear and withdrawal. The answer was 'Keep it one day at a time; don't take the first drink.' That advice was God-given, and it was for free, to sustain my life, to save my life.

I can have the elements – earth, air, fire, water – the basics. My life itself is free, God-given, and I live one day at a time – not tomorrow, next week, next year. That may be normal stuff for others but for me, an alcoholic, actually living it in my heart and soul it's special. In reality, I have to know I'm only living one breath at a time. Tomorrow may never come.

God, as I understand him, holds all tomorrows in his hands. Putting my will with His will takes discipline and hard work. No pain, no gain. We learn to love the pain. As with a boxer, you learn to love the pain. You know your pain's your friend. That's what you've got to go into. They're going to try and inflict pain on you. If you're used to it, you know how to respond to it.

So that's it. I've got this Step One, a day at a time. Maybe I'll want to drink, tomorrow, next week or next month or next year. I can give as much attention to that thought as I want but it's a waste of energy because tomorrow doesn't exist. *If* I arrive tomorrow, well I'll call it 'now' or 'today'. *I'm going to live my life one day at a time so if I don't drink today, I'll never take that first drink.*

Never drink? Why? Because it's always today so I don't have to beat myself up saying: 'Yeah, but I can't keep this up.' *I* don't have the future. My higher power has the future. I'm an alcoholic. I just accept all thoughts about drink as normal for me; as an alcoholic, what am I supposed to think about? Chocolate biscuits? If I think about anything, I think about drink. That's because my problem is drink. It's not cigarettes. It's not women. It's not gambling. It's drink.

I'm an alcoholic so if it was up to me, I'd take the drink sooner or later, but I hand it over to the Higher power and keep it one day at a time.

I go to meetings all over. I have a meeting at home, near where I live. If I'm in the north west – and I go up there a lot – I'll go to meetings there. I try to work the steps. I've made a beginning on the first four steps and I'm willing to do the rest.

I have had enough of trouble 'out there'. They were clapping me in with a bottle of Dom Perignon at Tramps when I won the title; in the steam baths there was an ice bucket and glasses on a tray. The dream came true.

Not long after that I was in the same club, fighting drunk and after that I was banned. The same man, but now mad with the disease of alcoholism. I had no power over it. I was insane. I finally accepted that.

I actually got into the door of the first meeting after asking my agent if he knew anybody who could help. He said he didn't but he knew somebody who did. So I rang up and went to a meeting. And now I accept that *my* mind is not the governing factor. I have to hand my will over to a Higher Power.

· EMMA GIBBS ·

◇

Emma Gibbs is SHARP's Fundraiser.

It's important that I start by saying that all I know today, I know with hindsight. My story is my story but the picture has become clearer during the seven and a half years that I have been sober. One of the greatest things about recovery from alcoholism is that it enables one to look back and discover and discard where necessary. I never knew how I 'felt' about things. Feelings were associated with hot, cold and warm. Today they run the whole range from joy to grief with many in-between.

I took the reins and got into the driving seat when I was five and a half years old. I remember the day in vivid detail. It was warm outside and my mother told me I could have any drink I wanted. That was the first indication there was something afoot because firstly her tone of voice was not celebratory and secondly I was only ever allowed soft drinks at the weekend and this was a week-day.

She had something to tell me and would I come into the drawing room. She told me my father was never coming back. My instant decision was to take care of her. To be responsible and 'grown-up' about it all, not to 'feel' anything. It was a devastating piece of news especially as I had always been very close to my father. I think subconsciously I thought it was my fault that he had left and that she would go as well unless I became a perfect child. I became the mistress of control. Drinking was out of the question and I never did drink until I was 23.

Occasionally I had a puff on a joint. I would try my hardest to have a glass of champagne at a wedding. In my late teens and early twenties it didn't worry me. People used to comment about my drinking coca cola. I used to say 'I don't drink' but then nobody ever said 'Why?'. I didn't like the taste of drink.

I didn't feel completely part of any crowd or scene. I had a very good job and I felt I was doing well. I was working on Vogue magazine which I went to when I was 19, staying there until I was 25, working my way up in the fashion department.

I didn't want to try drugs. They didn't interest me. And then I met a man who was very laid back. He took me out to dinner, asked me what I wanted to drink and I said coca cola. He said 'Have a glass of wine.' I wanted to impress him and didn't want to be different. I remember sitting in this restaurant in the Kings Road, holding my nose – to drink the glass of wine. That's when I started drinking and when I started taking cocaine.

The minute I took the coke that was it. That was the one, absolutely brilliant because it just enhanced all the feelings and made me feel superhuman. I realise today that was one of the only drugs I could find at the time that kept me in control. I never wanted to lose control. I did acid once but I never did smack, quaaludes, mandrax or any others.

In my peer group there were older people than me who said you could take it or leave it. But of course you took it and took it and I think for the next couple of years I could honestly say that I might have one or two drinks a week. Coke was very much for high days and holidays. Four of us might share a gram for someone's birthday. I was still doing very well at work which I'm sure fuelled a lot of my feelings of self-esteem.

I left Vogue and became European fashion editor on Women's Wear Daily, a very hard company, but I've always been an over-achiever. I always had terribly high expectations for myself and I thought others had very high expectations. I got the job in Paris, did it for a year and it wasn't my cup of tea.

While I was in Paris I did coke, but I never went out and found it. If it was there at a party I would do it and it was when I came back, I think, that the trouble started. The relationship was still continuing with the same man when I was in Paris – which had been wonderful because we saw each other at weekends and left each other alone during the week.

When I came back to London I lived with him which I'd never done before. I'd always had a bolt hole of my own. I felt very uncomfortable. I wasn't sure what I was going to do. For the first time, I felt lost – like a boat without a rudder, careerwise. For the first time since I was nineteen I thought 'What am I going to do? Where am I going to get myself work?' None of this I understood then. This has all come to light in recovery.

I went temping in an advertising agency and I actually enjoyed that but I didn't have a focus in my life. I'd had the job, I'd had the boyfriend. So I muddled along and quite enjoyed it. There were lots of young people and I didn't have too much responsibility. I stayed with that agency for years and ended up getting a permanent job with them.

Then, because one gets to know the right people, the coke starts to appear more and more and it was the most wonderful environment: it was all champagne and coke at the end of the day.

By this time my relationship with the man I had been living with was not good. We couldn't bear to be together and we couldn't bear to be apart. Then I started to have an affair with a married man and he did a lot of coke. That, I think, is where my habit took off. That's when I began buying it myself and I was always incredibly generous with it which I'm sure was my way of justifying my use of it. And that's when I started to want to be with people who either were doing coke or drinking.

I didn't like going home and being on my own. I'd either have people with me or go out to be with people. I began to be secretive about things and I began to dread letters from the bank and phone calls from people to whom I didn't want to talk. I think paranoia would be too strong a word at that stage, but I was definitely jumpy and probably miserable. I wasn't eating well. Although I didn't know it at the time, I began to look quite bad.

My skin would feel incredibly hot and then it would look very sore. I began to have constant hayfever or a cold and I probably got quite manic. I tend anyway to be a very up, full-of-energy person. I began to lie very deviously and towards the end of my using I used to tell quite incredible stories about people I'd known and people I'd been with.

I was getting into terrible trouble financially, running up huge overdrafts and avoiding the bank. The bank had a writ out against me and the writ-server managed to find me at the advertising agency. He took me to the pub and bought me a large vodka for a start before serving it. He explained what it was and said 'Be sensible . . . get hold of the bank, sit down and talk to them about all of this.' The only thing I minded was that they called me Spinster of This Parish.

The writ I threw in the bin. I thought 'I'll deal with that another time', because all my friends had large overdrafts. But they all had assets. I didn't. You would have thought I was Christina Onassis. I had five grandmothers who were about to die, leaving me a fortune. The bank somehow fell for it.

This all happened over a fairly quick period of time. I had never been good with money – until I got sober, maybe because nobody had ever sat me down and explained about banks. I don't blame anyone for that.

There were two people who were worried about me before I went into treatment. No one else suspected a thing, because I was just Emma. I was just a bit more over the top, a bit more amusing, a bit more bitchy. But as far as I could make out it wasn't that people didn't want to be with me. I might have become a *bit* of a drag, at the end of an evening, but no more of a drag than anyone else I was hanging out with. I mean, we all sat and psychobabbled until two in the morning. Sometimes when I got home I spent another two hours calling friends in Australia. Drink and dial, they call it. I even tracked down an old school friend at a lunch party outside Sydney. I didn't think it was a strange thing to do but she certainly got a shock.

Time passed. I went to a headhunting agency and soon I was running this agency on my own and holding the company cheque book. I began to supplement my income by going to the bank and cashing cheques. There was no-one to check on me. The woman who ran the company was in America. It was the perfect set-up for someone like me. I became more generous towards people. They all assumed I had a lot of money – if someone said 'Bring a bottle of wine' I would turn up with three bottles of champagne and two grams of coke.

To this day it astounds me that sometimes I would be carrying up to five grams of cocaine on me. I would collect it for a group of us. It never once crossed my mind that it was illegal or that I could be done for 'possession with intent to deal'.

Sometimes we'd go out to dinner and I'd pay for people because it was my way of wanting people to like me, and that was the only way I knew how to do it. I think I probably embarrassed people at times by my generosity but no one really questioned it.

And then they brought someone into the headhunting agency and I think then I knew the end was nigh. Again, I didn't know what to do about it. There were two cheque books on the go. One day the other woman picked up one of them and noticed there was a cheque missing out of the back of the book. I said the bank must have made the mistake and she replied 'Fine. I'll ring them up and ask them.'

As she picked up the phone I stood at the window and a voice said 'Actually, it's me.' It wasn't me who chose to say that. It was like another voice speaking through my mouth. I firmly believe that was the moment when my Higher Power (who had been there all my life) broke through the wall of denial I had built around me and decided it was time to take me by the scruff of the neck and give me a moment's clarity as to what was going on around me. Every recovering alcoholic I have ever heard talk always has this wonderful moment in their story when they say 'and then something happened'. This was when my 'something' happened.

I was terrified but I was also terribly relieved because I just couldn't stand it any more. It was my rock bottom. That was the moment when I knew that was it. I was going to have to face up to a whole lot of things. It was also coupled with an incredible arrogance that everything would be all right.

When I was told fraud charges were going to be brought against me, I called the only 'sensible' person I could think of – my sister. We had always been close as children but over the past few years I had drifted away from her (like I had from many old friends) because she was straight and very normal. Normal meant boring to me by this time but secretly it was what I really wanted.

She came round immediately. I seem to remember my explanation was that I 'was not good with money and got myself into a spot of trouble'. It is amazing how I had the ability to lessen the truth and thereby deny to myself the reality of the situation. She offered to try and help me and called someone to see if I could be bailed out financially. Another miracle happened. This person knew nothing of what was going on but simply said that there was probably more to this and that if I were to be bailed out now I would need bailing out again and again and that it was more important to get to the cause of it all. I will always be grateful to both my sister and the other person because they were instrumental in my getting sober.

I was terrified of telling the truth. It came out in dribs and drabs over the next few weeks but there was a lot more to come. My family were contacted and within three weeks I was in a treatment centre. The choice I was given was to either go there or out on to the streets. I was such a people-pleaser and so terrified of being put out in the cold that I just said yes. I didn't really know what treatment was. I had heard of people going to such centres and I supposed it was a good way of getting everyone off my back.

I went to Broadreach House in Plymouth. You can't get much further away from London than that! My family were convinced that I would never tell the truth. The treatment centre knew that I could and would when I was ready. Being able to tell the truth today is still one of the most important aspects of my life. It is a huge freedom to be able to do so even when I have got something wrong. I don't have to fight to prove I was right or justify my behaviour. That has taken a long time to change.

It was in the treatment centre that they suggested tentatively that maybe I had a drug problem and I was furious. But, again, I was *such* a people-pleaser that I *said* that was fine. I had an occasional pill, smoked an occasional joint. Night Nurse was my tipple. I would quite happily down half a bottle of that to make me sleep with a couple of extra drinks to calm me down.

I was in treatment seven weeks altogether. Disengaging from my family was hard to do because what I have is a family illness. Family sessions were encouraged in treatment and mine were pretty painful, but I began to learn that with time everything would settle down. I saw that my relationship with my mother needed to be dealt with, that I could no longer be the caretaker. I had to start looking after myself. I think I did learn a lot in treatment, much of which I didn't take on board at the time but I could understand that I did indeed have a drug problem and that I did have a drink problem and that I had no control once I started using.

When my seven weeks were up, I stayed in a bedsit near the treatment centre. I was on the dole and I think that was my second rock bottom. I had nothing – no money, no job. I was, however, eight weeks clean, but that was not what the ex-Vogue fashion editor had planned for herself at the age of 28. On top of that I had to go to self-help groups. I remember walking into a meeting full of ex-Marines or service sailors, plus two women who were lace-curtain drinkers. We seemed so different – they'd never been to a cocktail party and I'd never done a run ashore and got banged up for the night. But you know . . . East End boy meets West End girl.

I continued attending the meetings and after about a month I started to battle with the idea of being an alcoholic. I could accept being an addict – the illegality of it, the amount I was using, my behaviour patterns attached to the coke – but I didn't see myself as being an alcoholic, being like the people in meetings or like a down-and-out on a park bench.

It took me a long time to learn to live on £28 a week. I looked at a can of wine in a supermarket. I put it in my basket and thought 'What's the harm in it?' The frightening thing is that the first drink didn't have any effect, no great bolt of lightning or a booming voice saying 'I knew you would drink again.'

I didn't fall down drunk. That was when I learned that the first one is the one that does the damage. That went on for about three weeks. I was going to meetings drunk but not obviously so. I was spending all my time with other people in recovery. It was the worst three weeks of my life. I felt terrible physically but even worse emotionally. It was the absolute fear that I'd let everybody down and I'd failed again. The fear that if I told people, I'd be completely outcast and no one would want to talk to me. Eventually I was confronted by my counsellor. People began to say 'We think something's wrong.'

It was Friday, 13th July. It stuck in my mind because I was born on Friday, 13th January and I always wanted a birthday in the summer, and that's now my sober day, 13th July.

I went to see my counsellor and I hadn't had a drink. After about an hour of me denying I was drinking, he said 'Well, that's fine. I want you to come to after-care on Sunday'. They had somehow got everyone in treatment with me back that day. They came from Bristol, London . . . how they did it, I don't know. They were obviously worried.

I looked at all these people. I talked and no one bought it for a second. They all said 'We don't believe you but we care about you enough to sit here until you tell the truth, because you are going to get in real trouble if this carries on. You are going to die.' Eventually it all came out and that was another major turning point. I didn't get rejected. They thought I was worth saving. That terrified me because I didn't think I was worth saving.

I learned so much about my using once I got clean. A lot of the stuff about me I didn't realise until I'd been recovery for several years because I wasn't strong enough to see it and deal with it until then. I had a lot of family issues to deal with – relationships, friends, boyfriends, and so on. Some of them were tackled in counselling, very gently so as not to have me bouncing off the walls. It has been the most extraordinary on-going story.

By stages, making steady payments over a period of seven years, I have been dealing with my bank overdraft, relating my payments to my earnings, keeping in touch with the bank. Communicating. After all this time I have now paid off the overdraft.

My family relationships have improved. My stepmother has been the most amazing support now that I've got clean. She is the only person who has loved me unconditionally. She told me there was only one thing that she wanted me to know: 'If you drink again, I'm still going to love you. You can't stop me.' And no one had ever said that. She asked me what it was about recovery that still keeps you going to self-help groups after all this time. I said: 'I get such a kick out of it. It's given me everything I've always wanted to be and never could be. It's been the most amazing answer.'

It was two and a half years before I moved back to London. By that time I had been employed in a proper job and worked hard on myself. For my first year I had a very straightforward 9-5 job working in a psychiatric hospital. That's when I understood insanity. That's where I understood that my drinking had taken me and a lot of things like that have made me grateful. I'm grateful that I've got a recovery and that in my case alcohol and drugs didn't take me into an irredeemable state, either a wet brain or in a locked ward.

My life outside is good. I now see people I've got more in common with than just being in recovery, people with like-minded interests. I've got a whole group of friends who drink happily and socially and whom I need as much as the people in the programme, in order to have a balance in my life. I'm incredibly grateful I've got good social skills and don't have a problem being thrown into a dinner party with people I don't know. I do know how to talk to people.

What I find interesting is the level of conversation you have with people *not* in the fellowship. Whereas we would go in on such a deep level, I find it quite useful to be with other people were conversation is on a more superficial level. I need that too because you can get too much of this 'who am I, where am I, what am I?' stuff and I don't want to be eternally focussed on me. I need to be with 'normal' people.

I find you do rediscover old skills in recovery. I used to fear in early days that I wasn't going to have any fun or be with interesting people. I couldn't envisage the life I have now when I was down in Plymouth five years ago.

I'm becoming close to my family again. That has taken a long time but time is on my side if I don't pick up the first drink. Recovery is the most incredible journey and probably the first thing I have ever taken responsibility for in my life.

Last Saturday the sun was shining and I sat on my terrace and realised it needed cleaning and the plants needed dead-heading and I did it all. And I spent the day on my own. At the moment I'm very aware of the little things. The fact that I can put my mind to do something and do it. I no longer have to get angry or expect other people to do it for me. It can be done one step at a time.

• GARY GLITTER •

Gary Glitter is a rock musician and lives in London and Somerset.

At five o'clock, when you've had a heavy day, you get used to the idea of having a drink, to deal with the old stress factor. In the music business, there was always a drink before going on stage, and then it became pills, then it became cocaine. I know for a fact that I always enjoyed the idea of alcohol as opposed to cocaine. I used cocaine in order to support my alcoholism just so I could keep drinking.

I always drank. I grew up with drink. My stepfather used to sit me on the steps of the Silver Cross Pub opposite the Whitehall Theatre from the age of about nine, and it was always half a shandy or something like that. We always had wine with our meals.

So it was a way of life. I think that's the bad thing – that it's a way of life. I would rather somebody had encouraged me to go to a gym or something like that, as a way of life. Getting out of this habit was the hardest thing. When I went to Germany, to the Star Club and all those places, I discovered the pills because we had to work the first gig at seven at night and go through to seven in the morning.

It was a question of keeping awake, plus keeping that uplift. I always thought that you needed to have that uplift, that you always had to be the life and soul of the party. I've now discovered that I can go in somewhere and say, 'Look, I'm feeling miserable today, I don't care. You've got to accept it.' I don't have to be 'up' all the time. I *can't* be up all the time. I've got to have my down days like everybody else.

Back in the beginning, for quite a few years, it was a way of life. Everybody knew I drank. What you don't realise is that you start increasing your intake and the hangovers get heavier and heavier, until it reaches the stage of half a dozen special brews to keep you going until lunch, and there's a nice old slap-up lunch somewhere, and then you start collecting people, at the pub and the pub starts to come into your home. So there's a never-ending stream of people whom you don't know.

There was too much of everything. Champagne was a favourite because it had a very uplifting effect and went very well with my image. The extravagance shown by Gary Glitter shouting out for more champagne was exactly what I was trying to get across – the average person's idea of the way a pop star would behave. Being 'on' all the time – champagne and Lobster Thermidor all round.

I then lost my driving licence for a year. I was living in Hampshire at the time, but it didn't seem quite so bad as I could afford a chauffeur. It was good publicity and it had a rock'n'roll attitude about it. However, the next time was a three year ban and the third offence resulted in a five-year ban. The next time I could have gone to prison. I was so lucky that they didn't put me away because nowadays, three goes and it's mandatory. You go straight inside. And that time I was banned for ten years. So really, I've lost my licence for longer than I've ever driven. Thank goodness I never killed anybody. You always say 'I can handle it'.

The last time was the final straw because this was when everything in my life went wrong, really seriously wrong. First, the driving licence which was bad, especially with the threat and thought of going to prison. Then my girlfriend left me because – I am never, ever violent – I hit her, after a big champagne bout. She was going to leave anyway; she said she couldn't take it any longer. I was also working very hard to try and get my career back on footing, playing at universities. I was taking a lot of speed, coke and other stuff as well as drinking.

The court case and my girlfriend, leaving all came at once, I had one hell of a bash, a drinking session lasting about 48 hours and I really went to town. I think I took some coke and speed, as well, as alcohol. I ended up on the floor and could not move, just could not move. I think I cried for hours and hours, and I still could not move. I had to go to the loo and I literally had to crawl because I could not stand up. I could never understand why or what happened to me then. It almost felt like something spiritual happened. I spent a week lying on that floor and a particular space on it; I pissed and I crapped there. I felt so disgusted with myself because I was in such a terrible state on my own. I climbed up the stairs, got in the bath and little by little I managed; I still used that piece of floor as my security and kept going back to it. Eventually I worked it out that in order to talk to my girlfriend I'd have to be absolutely sober. The most important thing was to sort out my emotions so that I could make a few decisions about my life.

I really had to prove that I'd cleaned myself up, and of course anybody can do that overnight. It took me a long time to get back with her, over a year. She still watched me every moment, but because I had wanted very much to say how much I felt about her, it was like a dangling carrot in front of me, so one thing replaced the other.

I felt I had to get fit so I went running every day and I really enjoyed that. It was a kind of a high for me. It was an adrenalin high and it replaced the bottle with another carrot. It was something that I needed to do – basically to try and talk to my girlfriend. This was about six years ago and I haven't had a drink since.

After five years' disqualification you can re-apply for your licence. I was very lucky. I actually proved with the same psychiatrist I had used before and all the various different people that I don't drink and that not a drop has passed my lips. I was very pleased that the court gave me the break. It was very good, and it gave me a lift. They are so good at taking something away and it is very rare that they will give you something back. It was great.

I didn't go to AA or to any fellowship. I spoke about it quite a bit on television because when you've suddenly realised, you always try and explain to other people that actually they can have a better life without drink, without being wrecked. When I eventually went on stage, for once in my life I realised I enjoyed it. For so many years I wasn't enjoying going on the stage, I used to panic and get fearful. It was awful. As for being nervous, who cares if I'm nervous? Honesty was suddenly the great policy, trying to be honest with yourself and honest with people around you. Even as a performer I found I was enjoying it.

During the alcohol years and the drug years, the adrenalin never really got through. And it was enforced adrenalin; you get a quick charge and you think that's the adrenalin, but actually when you walk out at Wembley now, talk about adrenalin! Just by being there with the public, and everybody giving you that kind of energy. It's the most wonderful feeling in the world and you can only do it if you set yourself up with a bit of purity. I find that has happened with everything. I suppose it's just coming of age. I don't know.

You stop growing in every way when you're drinking heavily. And of course the pain that you cause other people is terrible. I've been getting stories over the years from my family and everybody else. They've been very good but I've caused so much trouble. I try not to walk around with the guilt – you've got to let it go and make amends where you can and say 'Sorry, I've made some mistakes, and I'm trying to rectify them really.'

I do see alcoholism as an illness. I now feel you should enjoy the moment, this is it. This is where we are. You may as well enjoy it. It's lovely. There was always that feeling in the past 'Oh I've got to be somewhere else.'

I did a breakfast TV show and one particular person was very kind, and said 'Do you want to have a chat? Here's my phone number, if you ever need to, ring me.' I thought that was fabulous, and now I do the same with other people. I've got friends who I've worked with, and so on. Their wives ring me up and ask how they can get it through to them. I say that's the hardest thing, to know that they've actually got to do it themselves. I've tried all sorts of things. I've said try and film him when he's being really obnoxious and let him see it. When my girlfriend left me, she did a tell' feature for a newspaper, because she was very upset. Having looked at it, I thought 'I know the kind of monster I'm made out to be,' and, in a way I was a monster, but I hadn't realised. Again I had to find out, and so in a funny sort of way, seeing that tabloid rubbish made me think it was a mirror, I had to think 'Am I as bad as that?' Very few people could get through to me.

And as for now, it's never been better.

· JIMMY GREAVES ·

Jimmy Greaves was an English international soccer player. He is now a television commentator and writer and lives in Essex.

I was a modest drinker in my youth. From my days as an apprentice professional at Chelsea I loved the camaraderie of the bar room. It was while at Chelsea that I developed a drinking habit, but it was certainly not a problem.

I can pinpoint the moment I doomed myself to life as an alcoholic. It was when I joined AC Milan. Suddenly I was a little boy lost and confused in the world of big football business and I began to use drink as a crutch. For over a year I was in a state of turmoil. I began to convince myself that I could cope more easily with my problems if I had a drink beside me. I was twenty.

I joined AC Milan for the money. I wanted to play football in Italy like I wanted a hole in the head. It was the worst year of my life and, little did I know it then, but it put me on the long and winding road to alcoholism. I was top scorer with nine goals in fourteen games, but I hated every second of the football. Most of the time I was badly depressed, ill with worry and I lost weight.

I moved from Milan to Tottenham Hotspur. They were the club I rated above all others. They had just become the first club this century to win the League and Cup double. After getting into my drinking stride in Milan, I can look back at the move to Tottenham as the period in my life when knocking back booze became a necessity.

A good drink was our reward for a job well done. Our manager, Bill Nicholson, and coach Eddie Bailey knew that several of us were pretty nifty with our elbows but never really appreciated the full extent of our drinking. As long as we were 100 per cent on the pitch and in training, they were content.

I began to divide my time between football, business and drinking. Bill Nicholson gave me a quiet fatherly word of warning about my drinking that went unheeded. Sir Alf Ramsey saw through me in five minutes flat. He was a shrewd judge of people who quickly had me weighed up as a carefree, nonconformist character whose thinking on football was completely the opposite of his.

Just before one of Alf's early games in charge of the England team when he was giving us the after-match agenda, I could sense that my drinking pals were waiting for me to act as their spokesman. 'A few of us were wondering,' I said 'Whether we could nip out for a couple of drinks before going back to the hotel.' Alf only swore when he wanted to make himself perfectly understood. 'If you want a fucking beer, you come back to the hotel and have it . . . ' It wasn't said in a nasty way but from that moment on Alf had me marked as a ring-leader of the drinking squad.

Time passed. Now that I can look back I can see clearly where and when I made my big mistake. I agreed to leave Tottenham. I cocked a dead ear to approaches from Brian Clough. I agreed to join West Ham. They had a drinking school there that could have taken on Tottenham and possibly drunk them under the table.

I was getting into an agitated state because I was not enjoying football at West Ham, but found that once I had a few drinks, my concern and worry drifted away. Suddenly football didn't matter to me any more. All I was interested in was drinking. Once I had five, six or seven lagers in me, I would get a click in my head and the world seemed a rosy place.

When I retired from football at the age of 31 it was like being let out of jail. It was free of all the discipline of the last sixteen years. For two years after quitting West Ham I was drinking solidly throughout the day, every day. By each lunchtime I would have poured several large vodkas down my throat on top of a minimum of six pints of beer. Lunchtime was a couple of Guinnesses, maybe a roll or a pub ploughman's and then a pint or more before closing time.

I would go home and sleep it off in an armchair before the evening assault on the bars of Upminster. At the end of the day I would have got through sixteen pints and anything up to eight or so shorts.

My wife Irene was appalled by the way I let my physical condition deteriorate. She was the first to realise I had a problem but I was too busy enjoying myself. At this stage I was financially secure. I kept up this pace for two years. And then the real drinking began. I started to smuggle bottles of vodka into the house and hide them.

I would never admit to a soul I was missing football. As long as I had a drink in my hand I was happy. But out of nowhere I was getting hit by deep depressions. All my frustrations at not being able to stop drinking used to manifest themselves in wild displays of anger. I broke windows, knocked doors off their hinges and occasionally tried to hit Irene.

She learned to judge my moods and knew when to keep out of my way. It must have been terrifying for her. I got into the habit of putting a bottle by the side of my bed so that I could have a drink first thing in the morning, to stop my hands shaking and to get my engine in working order for the day.

At the age of 34 I thought I would pack up drinking and play a lot of sport. Golf, squash, tennis and the occasional charity and Sunday matches. People would see me competing at sport and never believe that they were watching somebody who, within the past 48 hours, had knocked back two bottles of vodka and a couple of gallons of beer.

The drink was now costing me more than money. It was costing me the love of my wife, the respect of my kids and my standing in business. I went into a private nursing home for treatment and supervision. For a month they gradually reduced my craving for drink and I came out convinced that I had conquered the monster in one go.

Now I would drink in moderation. Just a couple of pints a day. But in no time at all the two pints became a couple of gallons and then it was back on the spirits. It was back in the nursing home and that is how I spent the next three years of my life as my world crashed around me.

A dozen times I went away for private treatment. I saw psychiatrists, paid out hundreds of pounds for advice and ignored it all. My doctor put me in touch with a fellowship of recovering alcoholics and I went along to a few meetings but wasn't impressed. I thought they talked a lot of waffle. Now they were people with a *real* drink problem. I wouldn't sink to that level.

But I did. I went out and drank again. Now I was at my rock bottom. Irene who had lovingly nursed me for two years had reached breaking point and could take no more. I moved in with my parents and used to call at home just to see the kids. I had clothes shops which went bust. I had a travel agency which is the worst possible business for an alcoholic because it requires a lot of PR – a ready-made excuse for drinking sessions.

Irene and I got divorced. There was no way our marriage could survive the pressure I put on it. I am assured that during my worst drinking bouts I was a pig of a man. I can recall the nightmare of the DTs, lying on my back shaking uncontrollably and having all sorts of terrifying hallucinations. I was in hell.

I once again turned to a fellowship of recovering alcoholics. Now I was able to say 'My name is Jimmy G. I am a professional footballer and I am an alcoholic.' I started to live life one day at a time, without a drink. The hell was over.

Irene and I got back together again, not back as a married couple, but loving each other all over again. I got a column in a newspaper, sold insurance and wrote a book *This One's on Me*. That was in 1979. I went on the Russell Harty show that year and told the viewers of my problem, how it was, what had happened and how it was now.

When it was over I felt like a released prisoner. I had been living in a tiny one-roomed flat in Wanstead and I was selling ladies' sweaters for a living. Irene saw the improvements in me and confidence returned and we are back living and loving together with the past tucked neatly out of the way. In time, the Sun gave me a column for my views on football and I was able to move out of the sweater business. Television work was offered and it led to Saint and Greavsie which in turn led to much else on television.

I am a grandfather several times over now. I haven't touched alcohol since 28th February 1978. I say a silent prayer to a power greater than myself for getting me into the second half of my life in reasonable shape, considering the liberties I have taken with my brain and body.

I leave you with this thought. It's a funny old life.

· ANTHONY HOPKINS ·

$\diamond$

Anthony Hopkins is an actor. He lives in London and Los Angeles.

I was in the Royal Artillery during National Service, a clerk for two years, stuck on Salisbury Plain. I watched a few men get drunk in the army but I didn't drink much. (I've often wondered about that.)

I went into the town on a Saturday night and sometimes I went into the NAAFI. I never had much money. I would have a couple of pints of beer, whatever I could afford. I didn't have any problem with drink then. I wasn't that interested. I was a bit of a loner; I didn't bother with anyone much. There were one or two friends and we'd go and have a couple of drinks. That was it.

When I came out of the army in October 1960, I got a job in Rep as an assistant stage manager at the Library Theatre, Manchester, with David Scase. Looking back on it now, I was surprised to find I still had this feeling that I dreaded authority. The stage director was very difficult and I suddenly felt that total incompetence again.

I threw a party (I can't remember where I had the money from) and I drank. That was the first time I was very ill from drink. I thought it was to do with mixing drinks.

I didn't experience any violent blackouts or any real doom until about the mid-Sixties when I was in Liverpool. (I was at RADA from 1961 to 1963. I drank my share there but there was no great catastrophe.)

I loved Liverpool. They were the happiest days of my life. It was at the time of The Beatles so it was buzzing and full of optimism. David Scase was a real champion for me.

Two people in my life championed me. One was in school – a rebel schoolmaster, Jim White. He was disliked by the staff and he in-spired terror in the kids. He had been in the RAF, bailed out and was taken prisoner. I realise now that a lot of the post-war schoolmasters had problems arising out of their wartime experiences.

I was an idiot at school. I didn't know what the hell was going on. I had a flair for English and I was quite artistic. One day I got into trouble. Somebody had been picking on and and I turned on him. I was very physically strong.

White said to me 'I don't want to see you doing that. You've got something. Now don't throw it away on this idiot. Don't lose that. Don't let people ride you. This place is sh . . . (you couldn't swear in those days). You stick to your own course. I'll be watching you but don't give them anything.' Jim White became my champion. I always admired him. There was something about him, very charismatic, an unpredictable man.

Scase, another great champion, fired me from Manchester where I was an ASM. He told me 'I'm going to have to let you go. I can't balance the books.' He gave a great raucous laugh and said 'You've got something. You've got a big presence on stage but I can't understand a word you're saying. You have no technique. I don't approve of drama school but why don't you go off to a good drama school, go to RADA, one of those posh ones. Learn your trade, because you don't know anything yet. You're a menace. You come on stage and you're dangerous; you hit people, you're out of control of your body. You certainly can't act like that but you've got this presence, this power.'

So I went off, deeply resentful. I went to Nottingham first – to hell with David Scase and his advice – but Roy Marsden advised me to go to RADA. When I came out I wrote to David. He was then at Liverpool. He auditioned people in London, at the Arts Theatre.

I was standing in the wings waiting to go on and the girl who was introducing the actors on stage called out and David said 'Have you improved?'

I said 'Well, I don't know.'

I did my piece and he said: 'That's good. That's better. Now that's how it should be; you've picked up something. You know your way around now. I'll give you a job.'

He was a marvellous champion for me because I was very into work, very intense. It was the best of times, that year. I was young. I had always felt out of sorts, rebellious, confused and unintellectual, but David, who was an ex-Merchant Navy man, very warm, and tough with no pretence about him, would help me. He'd demonstrate, he'd act out a part for you. He had a tremendous Rabelaisian way of behaving.

I then went to the National Theatre and I met all the top actors, the posh ones, and it took me years to get over the resentments. In those days you weren't spoken to – you were just a walk on. There was still a hierarchy. However, I got some parts out of Olivier and he liked me. But it was the beginning of a rocky time.

I went through a terrible marriage; I don't want to dwell on it. I left after two years because the marriage was a mess, my fault. I started drinking heavily but steadily, not drunk on stage but drinking. Nobody would notice because everyone else was in the pub at the interval or drinking before going on stage.

Olivier would say things to me like 'You mustn't drink while you're on stage' and I said: 'I'm not'. He'd say 'Well, you were in the bar at lunchtime and I'd reply 'Yeah, but that's lunchtime'. 'But you're going on stage with booze in you; you can't do that. The public aren't paying to watch you drunk. Don't drink!' That's what he was always telling us.

'If you want to after the show, then drink. I love to drink,' Olivier said, 'But you can't go on stage pissed.'

That was my loneliest period – 1965. I hated the Sixties. The loneliest time in my life. I was completely alien to everyone else and I had a deep hatred of all actors, the theatre and the acting profession – those I regarded as the 'posh actors'. I suppose it was what I thought of as The Establishment.

It was all resentment seething around. I disliked them all very much and felt no part of it and the funny thing is that I never really got through that. I still don't know what it is. When I'm working in the theatre I still feel that peculiar distance. But the resentment has gone now. The only thing I have in my mind now is that I'm thinking: 'Why can't I be like that? Why should they speak in a different language? I wish *I* could do that.' And now I think: 'Oh well, I can't.'

I did *The Lion in Winter* with Peter O'Toole and Katherine Hepburn in 1967, stuck around in films for a while and then I went back to the National in the 1970s and back to the old booze. That's when it really started getting bad. That's when I started getting into blackouts.

I met Jenni, who became my second wife. I remember the lovely summer of 1970. It was very romantic. We'd go off to a restaurant in our courting days, down to Richmond, or we'd go out rowing in a boat. There was always that five-thirty time, when everything got nice and muzzy . . . drinks on the river; fantastic.

Sometimes I'd go to rehearsal, then I'd go home. Jenni was working down in Pinewood at the time and I'd bring my script into the pub near where we lived, sit and have a couple of sandwiches and she'd join me at about seven o'clock for a glass of wine and I'd have a beer and sit there making my notes. It was very, very good.

There was the odd blackout and in the restaurant I'd order two bottles of wine and Jenni would say 'Two? I only want a glass.'

We'd go down to her parents and her father would have a bottle of Scotch in and I'd take it into the other room to do some work, be working on a script or something and he'd say to Jenni 'He doesn't half drink,' as if thinking ... well, he's an actor, you know ... of course actors have to drink. It's all part and parcel of being an actor – creating, and all that turmoil. It could be very pleasant and companionable, drinking.

Even in the good times though, there was always that 'sweat', I think, of 'Five-thirty' I would have a look at my watch – the pub should be open at five-thirty. I was always with people who were drinking. Some could handle it and I couldn't. I'd end up either belligerent or depressed. I could be very unpleasant.

I always turned on people who were nice and sensible. Actors who had a half-pint. Those were beneath contempt. And those actors who were good actors but weren't threatening – gentle, nice people. They had a horrible mauling. They were my targets. It was Jekyll and Hyde. But some of the time it was a lot of fun as well.

When I left for New York to do the play *Equus*, that's when it became very frightening. I was on the rollercoaster then. My wife Jenni was with me and that's when it started to scare her. There are all those bars. It's heaven and hell, madness in the air, wonderful bars and large measures.

On my first day in New York in August 1974, a young man came to interview me; he was a wonderful audience for me because he was a fan. I took him into the bar and we got smashed. I had to go to a party that night. John Dexter was there and the American cast, and I finished up telling Peter Shaffer what was wrong with his play, but he was very tolerant. I started rehearsing and it was a big hit. And I was in the bars; I just couldn't stay out of them; they were a magnetic force.

I was thrown out of one bar, told they wouldn't serve me. There were blackouts, too. We had an apartment, East 54th Street, between Park and Lexington; I knew it like a mantra so that I could get home by cab.

We had an eight-month run with the play. With the bars it was a hell of a struggle. I had six dry weeks. I had a scare and met someone from AA called Mary who was in the play; she just let me fall about. She didn't try to interfere.

She told her ex-husband who was also a member of AA that she was working with someone who was a drunk and he said: 'Oh let it go, don't interfere with it. You know better than that. Even if it is terrifying, let him fall on his arse.'

And I did a few times. I was at a party once; I got into such bad shape. I'd been smoking grass as well; it was like I was standing over the brink of hell. I was standing against a wall, and I was afraid to move in case I fell into a hole which wasn't there, a big bright white hole. It was then I asked her if she could help me.

She told me about it the next day. She told me all about AA, and about the progression of the illness – almost in an infant school way. It's like travelling on an elevator from the top floor down to the basement, or from Park Avenue to the Bowery on the train. You can get off wherever you choose, any time.

She told me those silly little things. Don't take the first drink, you won't get drunk. I thought how simple-minded. She asked me if I would like to go to a meeting. I said: 'No, no, meetings, no no.' Meetings, tambourine, nice smiling ladies, cups of tea and charity . . . I said: 'No, I'll be OK, I'll do it my way.'

So I did six weeks on my own and my trousers started fitting me because I was losing weight and I was looking really good, got a bit of a suntan, walked to work, had tremendous energy. I thought my God, this is no problem. I'd drink gallons of Perrier water or whatever the equivalent was. Then, go into restaurants . . . 'Whisky or gin? Certainly not. Large soda water please. Make it a double.' Mary could see me; she knew how to play it. 'Good for you.' She let go.

At the last night party in New York, there was a celebration with a bunch of people to say 'Goodbye' to me; I was on my way to California and they were welcoming the actor coming in to take over, Anthony Perkins. I remember standing by a big sideboard in this apartment on Central Park South, thinking, well just one glass, a little bit of whisky.

Six months later, I was in California, drinking tequila. I loved it. It seemed to give insights; you could hallucinate.

I was doing a film with Elizabeth Montgomery, *Dark Victory*, a remake of the old Bette Davis film. I decided to live there and that's when I applied for my green card. I was courting disaster because I had learned to drive out there and the immigration guys keep an eye on you. You have to keep your nose clean, and if you got out of line (with, say, drink driving) then you'd be in trouble.

I was doing all sorts of daft things that could have got me out of the country. Driving over the canyons, blacked-out, getting home at night not knowing where the hell I'd been, whole nights had gone in my mind. I couldn't remember how I got back. In the mornings, I'd be wondering all the time 'Had I killed somebody?' I would check the front of the car.

Jenni decided she would come back to England to give herself a break, to get away for Christmas. That was the best thing she ever did. She's never nagged me. She did all the right things, but inside she was in agony. I could hear her crying. She loved me and she was trying to keep it all together and I was trying to keep it all apart, with viciousness and hatred, 'This silly woman. Can't she see how it is for me?'

I had terrible self pity. She just had to admit defeat and go home for Christmas. The night before she left, I said 'While you're away, I'm going to look into this matter of AA,' and she said, 'Why is that?' And I said 'I think I'm an alcoholic.' 'Oh.' Well, she was weary.

She didn't rise to it, didn't say 'Oh good.' It was like a cold indifference. I took her to the airport, she went off. Rather cold . . . 'Well have a nice Christmas.' I said: 'And you. Love to your parents.' That was it.

I got well and truly smashed that night. The next day, I took off and drove all the way down to Phoenix, Arizona, and I spent Christmas Eve and Christmas Day in a filthy hotel. I didn't know what the hell I was doing there.

I was sitting in the bar at night playing the juke box, Neil Sedaka's *Solitaire* and Billie Holliday. It had come to this? It was such a foul hotel. I remember there was blood on the pavement outside. And there were fleas.

I drove back to LA on the 27th, a Saturday night, to an empty flat. I went down to Beverly Glen market, and got my bottle of tequila and my big jar of orange juice to mix up a nice big cocktail.

I stood at the counter behind a big fat woman who was chatting to the cashier; they looked at my brown bag I think, and she said 'Oh yes. They think it's a disease now. Alcoholism. I was reading about it in the paper.'

I thought 'Are they talking about *me*?' I went back to the apartment and I sat there watching the lengthening shadows across the wall of the courtyard. I felt the dreadful loneliness of the alcoholic, the feeling of the alcoholic who's thrown everything away. His marriage, his life and everything. I thought 'Well, I've always been a bit of a drama queen, you know – I'm an actor. Maybe I'm making too much of it, but it seems I'm losing everything.' I looked up and thought 'My God, what am I *doing*? It's this stuff. Why can't I stop?'

And then the phone rang and it was somebody inviting me to a party, so the next thing I remember is being at a beautiful house in Beverly Hills. It was a big party; another British actor was there and I was in the garden with him, shouting and raving. We were both pretty drunk, saying 'I'm a better actor than you are.' The next thing I remember is sitting on a sofa with somebody talking to me. It was my agent at the time and he said: 'Come on. I think you ought to go home.' I stood on the doorstep and couldn't find my car.

I said 'Somebody's stolen my car.' The hostess said 'Now Tony. Calm down. You drove up here, blew your horn and then vanished and we came looking for you. Then you called and asked could somebody come to pick you up. You said that you'd lost your car in the middle of the street. Sandy came and got you.' Why they bothered to bring me to the party I don't know. I was raving.

Or maybe I wasn't. Maybe it had got to that stage where it doesn't show.

I said to my agent 'I think I'm an alcoholic, and I think I need help. Can I come and stay with you?' He replied 'Yes of course.' I said 'I'm scared to go back to the apartment.' We got back to his house in Beverly Hills' Benedict Canyon and I repeated 'I'm an alcoholic. I need help.' 'He said 'AA?' 'Yes.'

He got me the number of AA and I sat up until about four o'clock, rambling on until I was sober. Something had happened. *And* I had this number in my pocket.

I went back to my apartment in the morning and, sure enough, the Mexican janitor who looked after the building said: 'Mr Hopkins. Your car – I picked it up off the street.' I apologised. He said 'That's all right. You were crazy last night. That's OK.' The car was worn out.

On that Sunday I just sat in the apartment. There was no itchiness. Just a kind of flatness. I now knew what I was and I had to do something about it. I didn't phone AA that day because I thought they would be closed (on a Sunday). So, I phoned them the next day and a woman called Dorothy answered. I said 'I need help. I think I'm an alcoholic.' She said 'Oh that's good.' I thought 'These people are weird.'

I went out and walked across the old tracks on Santa Monica Boulevard and, as I was going across, I thought do I really *know* that I'm an alcoholic, but another voice over-rode it saying *'Go and do something now.'* I went up the stairs to this office and I expected to see men in white coats, and others in dirty raincoats, and I expected to see that guy who played the heavy in Charlie Chaplin films but really the only person who was there was Dorothy.

She asked if I was Tony. I said 'Yes.' She said 'How are you? I've seen you. You're an actor aren't you? How can I help you?'

'I'm an alcoholic.'

'Well, good.'

'Well, it's not so good for me that I'm an alcoholic.'

'Well it's good that you found out you are.'

I asked her if she was an alcoholic and she said she wasn't but her husband was – and is. They were divorced but she worked as a volunteer for AA. She was a Christian, worked in the local church and wanted to help out. I asked her what I should do and she said 'Give me your phone number, and I'll get somebody to come out and collect you and take you to a meeting tonight.'

I said 'Meetings?' She said 'Yeah. Meetings.'

'AA meetings?'

'That's right.'

'Whereabouts?'

'Never mind whereabouts. Just go.'

I gave her my number. She asked me whether I had any drink in the house and I said I had a couple of beers in the fridge and she suggested I should pour them down the drain. I wanted to cry because she was being so kind. I told her I'd pour them away.

'I promise. I don't want to drink.'

'I know. I know.'

She told me just to go home and rest. 'You've been out there fighting long enough.' I didn't know whether I could cope. I knew she was gong to spring the word on me. She said 'Why don't you just try . . .' I *knew* what she was going to say: 'Why don't you just trust in God.'

I was so relieved. She had given me permission to open the door. It's as though the door was slightly ajar but I was scared to push it. But I wanted so desperately for somebody somewhere to help, and the door opened. I got very tearful and said 'I'll call you later.'

The most extraordinary thing happened actually, as I was standing there on Westwood Boulevard, a bright sunny day, 29th December 1975, I realised that something had happened that was going to change me. I didn't know why. But at least I had done something which was not of my own will. An attitude had been lost.

I felt this tremendous relief and a very powerful force which was almost like a vocal form, like big newscast in my head. It said 'It's over. Now you can start living. Get on with your life. Don't forget one second of it because it's all been for a purpose.'

And it was at that moment that I felt accepted. I thought I belonged. I said to myself 'I have a right to be here.' And I didn't know where these thoughts came from.

That night I was picked up by George C. He came to the apartment with his girlfriend. He was everything I expected him to be: pale blue jacket, iron grey hair, like Lloyd Bridges, smelling of after-shave lotion. I thought 'This is it; I'm in with the Moonies now.' He said 'Hi. Howdy.' I sat in the back of their car and I thought 'They're going to mention Jesus at any moment now, but I don't care.'

I didn't care what they talked about; and I walked into the meeting, a big meeting in The Palisades which became my home group. Somebody came over to me and said 'Hi Tony! My name is Bob. We worked together last year. I came to pick you up; I was working for ABC Publicity.' He became my sponsor.

I said 'Yes. That's right.' He asked 'How're you doing?' I said 'Oh, I'm terrible.' He said 'Good. I've got a chair waiting for you here. Come on over.' I saw another actor whom I'd worked with just a few months before. he said 'Hello Tony. I'm really glad to see you here. I knew you were in bad shape when we were working together. You ought to hang around, because you'll just get crazy like the rest of us but you'll get better and you don't have to drink.'

To me, the image of an alcoholic was something from *Lost Weekend* but in a brightly lit bar somewhere, with an empty glass and ashtrays full of cigarette ends in a sort of permanent night, somebody emaciated, with his collar up. I just saw movie actors, looking seedy.

At that first meeting I sat down in the chair they offered me with these two men sitting next to me, George and Bob, and I knew I was home somehow. I knew something was up. And somebody got up and read Chapter Five from the Big Book and people would say their name 'My name is Joe and I'm an alcoholic' and the others would say 'Hi Joe.' Wonderful. Such support.

And the first speaker, from Palos Verdes, Dr Don with lank hair and a growling voice, 'Hi, my name is Don, and I'm an alcoholic . . .' I thought: 'God! That's it. That's him. The Alcoholic!'

He said he'd been sober for about fifteen years and this voice came out, 'I'll tell you how bad it got, folks. I was in the middle of a surgery, in the middle of a blackout and I came to and I wasn't sure whether I had to stitch the guy up or open him up. That was my bottom.' And everyone laughed! I started laughing.

Then Chuck C spoke after the interval, talking about resentments and two people spoke about feeling on the 'outside of things' all their lives, how they tried to control things but they could never keep anything balanced. Everything was falling apart all the time yet somehow they tried to keep going.

I thought, 'God. All those feelings I'd had ever since I was a four-year-old kid standing at the top of the street. Never making things add up. That's what it was like. And all these people knew what it was like to feel like that!'

My instincts were open enough that night for me to say (to myself) 'So *that's* why I drank. I had to drink to stop myself going crazy.' And it all made sense after that.

It's not a moral disease, it's just a peculiar condition. A condition of disorder. That's why I drank. And when they mentioned the word 'God' that also made sense; being an atheist didn't make any sense at all.

It all started coming clear. My mind started opening up like windows. Light poured in. I was introduced to Chuck C afterwards and George said 'This is Tony. It's his first day.' Chuck put his hands on me and said 'You just keep coming back because we get better that way. We're the luckiest people in the world. We get better and better. Don't you forget that.' I said 'OK.'

I knew it was over. I knew that I was in contact with something phenomenal. The first few months were kind of electrifying. I smelled smells. I saw colours and I said to Jenni 'The grass is green'. She got very angry and said 'Of course it's green.'

She had an awkward time in the first months of recovery. She's not in Al Anon. Chuck C said to me 'It's none of your goddam business. She's not an alcoholic. She's not in Al Anon, maybe it's not for her. You're not running her life. Let go.'

He told me to go home, and stay sober. I had been given permission to live.

· ELLEN JAMESON ·

*Ellen Jameson is a journalist and broadcaster living in
London and Brighton.*

My drinking started when I first came to London. It seemed everyone was out to get to a bigger and better party.

I started drinking scotch and coke because apparently that's what
the Beatles drank. I was one of those who was never going to start
drinking because I knew what it did for my family. The joke was
when everybody else was drinking alcohol, I was drinking tea. I just
didn't want anything to do with alcohol.

As a child growing up, I knew what the problems were. I had loving parents who were absolutely wonderful, but when they took a
drink, everything changed. All our lives went into chaos and so I was
determined not to touch it. Then suddenly I started drinking. I was
19.

My favourite had always been coca cola and then someone said to
me 'The Beatles put whisky in their coke'. I thought 'If it's good
enough for them, it's good enough for me.' Easy to say and do, but it
didn't taste nice. Right to the end of my drinking, I didn't like the
taste of the drink. I was still a fussy alcoholic. I was still saying: 'Could
I have some lemonade in this?' or 'Is there any coca cola?' I never
liked the taste but I loved the effect.

At that time it was all go in the pop world, receptions and parties.
There wasn't any question of money. We would go to receptions
where yards of whisky were poured, topped up with coke. For a long
time I didn't know how much I was drinking.

It was the late sixties and by the age of 20 I was married to Gavin.
We were both journalists in the pop world, drinking champagne on
river boats and things like that, not cider under the arches. It was the
glamorous world of drinking. And somehow it seemed to be OK. At
that time all my friends were in that circle and there were always
those who stayed on at the parties later.

I was one of those who, when the party finished, went on to
another party and then to a club and then to somewhere else. By

now Gavin was editor of Disc magazine and it was a case of 'Four o'clock; right. Where are we going tonight? Polydor have got this at so and so and this one's got one there.' There might be five events going on. 'Right – we'll look in on all of them.'

Everyone wanted to give a better party than the last person and that involved loads of free booze. There must have been people in those days who didn't drink but I didn't know them.

In those early days the hangovers were pretty ferocious. I remember about four months after I started drinking, each step I took my head was going bang, bang, bang! One bang after another. I still didn't know. In those days I thought the problem was *me*. As soon as I got a drink inside me, I could talk to anybody, go anywhere, do anything.

Whenever people talk in meetings I switch backwards and forwards because I honestly believe now that if I hadn't drunk then, I could have had a wonderful time. All those places I went to. It would have been better without drinking.

At the same time drinking *was* a lot of fun then. There was a lot of social drinking and it just seemed that everybody else drank as much as I did. I don't know what their heads were like the next day. It was just that that was the scene at that time.

Working in journalism, you met everyone in pubs, clubs and restaurants. You did your interviews there. Talking to people and drinking. Your drinks were being paid for on your expenses. It seemed implicit in the job. In newspaper terms, the message seemed to be 'If you're pissed, keep your head down.'

That was it. If you went back to the office drunk there was a good chance of concealment. I knew plenty of quiet places where you could put your head down or someone would put you in a cab and send you home. *Or* someone would take you back out to another drinking club. I don't recall anyone in those days ever saying to me that I had drink problem.

Since getter sober I've often thought of the jobs I wanted that other people seemed to get. Or the title, or the promotion. I would be in the pub complaining: 'Why didn't *I* get it?' Afterwards you realise you were always in the wrong place. You weren't in the office.

Then, of course, it says in the Big Book of AA that when you see what most of us have achieved drunk . . . you could fly when sober. I was working right up to the day when I got to the fellowship. Unfortunately the drink had got worse.

As with everybody else, there were times when I said: 'Right. That's it. I'm on a diet. I'm not drinking.' I told people I was on antibiotics but I never managed to stop drinking for more than a couple of days. People watched out for me, trying to see which drink it was that 'did it'. I never got it into my head that it was the *first* drink that did the damage; that started it. My drinking became progressively worse. By now my marriage was over and I met Derek who was to be my second husband. He was part of the 'Fleet Street Scene' with all its heavy drinkers but thankfully for me, he hardly drank at all. Not because he particularly disapproved. Drink wasn't that important to him.

I suppose I knew I had a problem when, on my thirtieth birthday, I tried to commit suicide. I had always claimed that I wouldn't live past thirty. I suppose the thought came from others, like Marc Bolan. We all reckoned 'I won't need this body after thirty. It's OK to abuse it. I'm gonna be gone anyway.'

So when I got to 30 and I was still here, I tried to commit suicide. That was just one of several attempts. And when I sobered up, I did go to a self-help group, based on the twelve steps. I tried to find out what the problem was. I didn't think it was the drink. I thought I was 'depressed'. At the meeting I thought what nice people they were, like Jehovah's Witnesses. But not for me.

I still saw myself as a high flier and after a period without drink, I poured another and stayed 'out there' drinking for another six years when, again, I phoned the fellowship.

They said 'Well, has it got better?' I replied 'Are you crazy? It has been awful. I'm going demented, I don't know what to do with myself.' I was in such a mess. They said 'Why don't you go to a meeting?' I said 'I went to one and it didn't work.' I was ready by this time. I was sick and tired of being sick and tired.

The mental thing was the biggest problem. I was going out of my head. I knew Derek wouldn't put up with much more. I was out of touch with the world. I used to walk around the flat with a large drink in my hand saying 'God, what have you done to me?' I didn't want to answer the telephone. I didn't know whom I'd spoken to the previous day. I didn't dare answer the door because I didn't know who I'd taken up with.

I was in total fear.

At one stage, Derek said to me 'Why do you never even apologise? Why do you pretend the next day that everything's OK?' I didn't know. Maybe I thought that if he didn't say anything I'd got away with it. Now it all seems so sad.

I said to him 'Why did you stay with me? Why did you love me?' He said 'Because I knew you. I knew the *real* Ellen.' He saw the drink was dragging me away but he was determined not to let me go. That was one of the amazing things. When I would say 'Just give up, just go for God's sake; just leave', he wouldn't.

Of course I wanted a bit of freedom as well. I had a dream of going and staying in a little seaside hotel and drinking, where nobody would bother me. I wanted him to let me go. But he wouldn't. He had decided he would hang in there until I got well.

There is a lovely story of Derek going to a gypsy in Blackpool. She said, 'Your partner's very sick' and he said 'Yes she is, but it's not a normal kind of sickness.' The woman said 'Yes. It's the drink.' He told her she was right and she said 'She'll stop one day; one day she'll just stop.' It took another six years.

He waited, one day at a time. He is wonderful because on the day I joined the fellowship for proper, six years later, I came home and told him where I'd been and he said 'Thank God it's over.' I said 'Well, I don't know. It sounds like a pretty tall order. So today I'm going to try not to pick up another drink.' and he said 'No. It's OK. The storm is finished.'

A couple of months later he said to me: 'Let's get married.' I said 'I can't. The fellowship recommends you don't make any major life changes for two years after getting into sobriety. I don't want to do anything against what they're suggesting.' Two years later he asked me again. I was very lucky. I said 'I'd love to.'

It is the only thing that's ever worked for me. Being abstinent is the only thing that's ever given me any real happiness. I'm like so many other people. I came to London from the North and I was wide-eyed and everybody else seemed so confident. I was the only one who wasn't, but with a couple of drinks then I was as confident as them. It never occurred to me that maybe they had any kind of fears or hang-ups. I just wanted to be part of the crowd. I didn't realise that someone like me who has a propensity towards alcoholism is going to get caught.

And that's what so frightening. That the disease was there and so rampant in me, that the power of denial was huge. I used to scream at Derek 'Don't talk to me about the drink. Let's talk about why I'm unhappy? Why am I unfulfilled? Why am I depressed? Why do I never get the jobs I want? Let's put the drink on one side.'

He always attacked the drink, but that was the very thing that I had to defend. I suspect that somewhere deep down inside I knew what was wrong. I knew that only when I admitted it, would I stop.

I went to my first meeting. Someone was doing the chair and it clicked. A light went on in my head, I came home and said 'It's the drink. Why did nobody ever tell me?' I then knew that the depression came out of the bottle. The mental problems came out of the bottle and the physical problems came out of the bottle.

Only as I got more sober could I keep tracing it further and further back to when I started drinking. I never drank like an ordinary person. I always wanted to get drunk. Not liking the taste of it, I needed the sensation. I always wanted to be high.

In those early days of sobriety there was so much fun in getting back in touch with reality and with a world one didn't really know. I used to think 'How am I going to tell everybody that I don't drink?' It's astonishing the number of people who just didn't seem to notice, people whom I thought must have known I had a drink problem. When I went to their house, they would say 'What are you drinking?'. I'd ask for a Perrier and they'd say 'Fine.'

I, however, had prepared a long speech to explain everything. Really, people don't take that much notice. I had a situation where I hadn't had a drink for a couple of months and I was at a party and somebody came up and asked had I started drinking again? I said 'No. I haven't.' And they said, 'You're so happy.' 'Yes', I said, 'I am. This is me without drink.' I'm laughing. I'm chatting. After my own wedding, somebody said to me 'You were drinking weren't you?' I said 'There wouldn't have been a wedding if I'd been drinking.' And they said 'But you were laughing and dancing.' And I said 'Yes, I know. It's possible to do those things without drinking.'

There's an idea out there that champagne is 'OK'. People say 'You can have a glass of champagne, can't you? What harm could that do?' Now I had never identified *alcohol* as the problem. I had identified say whisky or gin or maybe that Australian wine was a bit off. Or this red wine gave me a headache. I never identified alcohol *per se* as the cause of trouble. And then I got to the fellowship and read: 'Powerless over alcohol' and thought 'Oh no! Alcohol!'

In the past I'd tried so often to stop drinking and be a good girl, get Derek talking to me again, and catch up with the work. I'd say 'I'm gonna be good, I'm gonna be good.' Then, 'I think I'll have a shandy' or 'I'll just have a glass of wine.' I honestly did not know that it was that one shandy, that one glass of wine that started the binges.

If I didn't have a drink for two days and still lost my temper, swore or dropped something, I'd say 'See. It's not drink. I haven't had a drink for two days and yet this is still happening to me. So this is *me*. So I might as well drink because I'm like this anyway.'

What I didn't know was that the minute I put a bit of alcohol into me I was a goner. Now that I'm in touch with reality I've discovered that the three-hour traffic jam that I used to get caught in has gone. I don't know where it went to. I haven't experienced it since I got sober. Trains that suddenly 'don't appear' seem always to turn up now that I'm sober. All of that world that I thought was so chaotic in fact wasn't. *It was only Ellen who was chaotic.* I always left somewhere an hour after I should have been at the other place and that's why the 'traffic jams' were so bad. That's why the trains never came. That's why, if I stood on the corner for three minutes and the cab didn't come, I'd go back into the pub and say: 'Oh well. You know, you can't get a cab in London for love or money.' On Wednesday afternoon!

I think what happened was that I spent most of my last six months drinking and trying not to drink. And so I would have three days on, two days off, a week on, a week off, and so on. On Derby Day 1986 I hadn't had a drink for a couple of days. We were going to Epsom in the car and Derek said to me 'I hope you're not going to start drinking again.' I said 'Oh, don't start. Don't spoil the day before we get there.' But of course, I did drink.

I telephoned a number where I could get in touch with a fellowship of recovering alcoholics and at that point they said: 'Do you want someone to come and see you.' I didn't. What happened was I drank another weekend.

We were with some friends and on the Sunday Derek said to me 'Well?' I had woken up and found everything 'fine'. Clothes off and hung up, so life was going to be OK, you know; you are where you should be and everything seemed all right.

By this stage much of my drinking was blacked out anyway. As long as I was where I should be when I woke, then I didn't know if anything had gone wrong in the previous evening.

Then Derek said to me 'I never thought I'd see you falling out with her.' 'What are you talking about?' He said 'Ellen. If you don't remember it, you've got a bad problem.'

I kept trying to piece the evening together. I could not find that 'falling out' anywhere. I thought he was winding me up. I phoned my friend and asked 'Did I fall out with you?' She said 'It's OK. It really doesn't matter.' I said 'Well it does matter.' She was sort of my mentor at that time, giving me a lot of spiritual guidance. However, most of the spirit was coming out of the bottle. She was somebody I looked up to. I really couldn't believe that I had abused her and fallen out with her. But they told me I had. That terrified me because that was a totally identifiable thing where I had a large hole.

I had one more weekend of drinking. I finished off that weekend and woke in this person's house in a baby's cot with my boots and all my clothes on and I just cried. I just thought 'what have I come to? What is going on?' When I'd gone for that 'Sunday lunchtime drink', ha, ha. Derek had said to me 'Watch the gravy. *Do* watch the gravy.' Of course, what happened was what always happened. I'd been on the phone to him every hour. 'I'll be back any minute.' By six o'clock on Sunday evening, when I was supposed to be cooking a joint of meat for our dinner, I was saying 'Oh, the baby's lying on my coat so I can't leave now.' I woke in the cot next day and when I looked in the mirror I had crayon all over my face. I had let the baby draw all over me.

I came back from there and picked up a couple of cans of lager to 'straighten me up' and I stood in the bathroom drinking it. I was thinking 'Derek's on the radio till 9-30 am' and this was sometime after nine o'clock. I didn't know how long it took him to get home from there. I didn't know if it took ten minutes or ten hours. I just had no idea. All I knew was if he wasn't on the radio he might suddenly appear in the house. I just never knew what was going on.

I stood in the bathroom at nine o'clock in the morning, forcing down a can of lager just to give me *enough*, just to stop the shakes long enough to get on with some work. I was crying.

I do believe that was my spiritual awakening. That was my rock bottom. I just said 'God. You've got to do something for me. I can't go on like this. I'm going demented. I'm staggering from day to day and I don't know whether I'm coming or going.'

Having a sober suffering partner in there, loving you, is such a support. Every day you're saying 'Sorry, I'm sorry. It won't happen again. I really honestly tried.' Those last ten days spent in and out of blackouts began to sow the seeds. Within two weeks I was in the fellowship, and that was after I hadn't come home again. I was due home. And I came home a day late.

I found a note from Derek which said 'You are a mess. The office has been phoning all day. There's no cat food. There's no food in the house. I've gone to Birmingham as arranged. I'll see you when I see you.'

That brought it all home to me. That was the mess of my life in one go. All of these phone calls were people I was trying to avoid anyway. The cat was hungry. The food would come from the off-licence in any case. When Derek came back from Birmingham, I was in the bath and that was one of those days when I was covered in bruises. 'How did I get these? I don't know where these came from.' I used to say 'Please God, give me one week without any bruises, when I can look back from Tuesday to Tuesday and everything is fine.'

Finally I was in the bath and it was like a scene from *Alice in Wonderland*. The tears were running down my face. They were huge. I thought I was going to drown in my own tears. Derek came into the bathroom and I said to him 'Just go. It is never going to get any better. I'm rotten through and through. You're going to have a lot of heartache if you stay.' And he grabbed me by the shoulders and said 'You're sick Ellen. You're so sick. They can help people like you. Let them help you.'

I said 'What are people like me?'

'You're an alcoholic.'

I said 'I'll try.'

When he said they could help people like me, I desperately needed help. If he'd said I was a Martian, I'd gladly have gone to the embassy for Martians. I'd have done anything just to get out of the hell.

So to go the fellowship and be told 'You're not bad' is the most miraculous thing. I was prepared to say that I was the worst person in the world and they said 'You're not, Ellen. You're a sick girl. We can help you.'

I came out of that meeting and I went back to the bathroom. I got down on my knees and said 'God, you probably don't remember me, but my name's Ellen. You've kept those other alcoholics sober. Would you do it for me? Just for today.'

And I've never had another drink.

· JULIA ·

Julia is a writer and lives in London.

I came from the kind of home where people didn't drink excessively. I was taught to drink by being given a small glass of Dubonnet every now and again in my teenage years. I went to teenage parties where there was something like cider cup to drink, so I didn't meet alcohol in a free and easy way until I went to university. Cambridge. There I met it and enjoyed it. There was a certain amount of drugs around Cambridge at that stage. There wasn't the heavy stuff. There was, interestingly, very little pot either, but there were amphetamines, purple hearts. I had a friend who took quite a lot of those, and another friend who took a lot of pot which they got in a very complicated way from American servicemen, but though I tried both on maybe two occasions, I remember thinking, I could get into trouble doing this, I could be sent down, it's illegal, and why bother when there's alcohol.

Already I was seeing alcohol as fun. And indeed I had a lot of fun. I enjoyed getting drunk and I can't think of any other reason for drinking. What would otherwise be the point? I suppose I was occasionally an excessive drinker. It affected my love life marginally at this point but I can't think it caused much trouble. I didn't do a lot of work and I partied a lot, but I think that was as much making up for feeling unsuccessful at social life earlier in my teens as it was to do with alcohol.

When I was a teenager, we'd moved to a very snobbish district and my father had severe social insecurity. I would go to teenage parties and he'd ask who I'd danced with and, if he thought the boy I'd danced with wasn't one of the posher Gloucestershire set, he would think that wasn't good. So it was all rather an ordeal. I must admit I desperately wanted a boyfriend and I didn't meet any boys I liked because they all seemed to be hunting, shooting and fishing while I was an incipient intellectual. I felt out of place.

So when I got to Cambridge, the intellectual men – lots of them, ten to one at that time – seemed like heaven. Alcohol didn't play a very large part then, though there was one occasion when I got very drunk and had to be put to bed. However, there are lots of people who have that sort of experience and don't become alcoholics.

After Cambridge I went to Fleet Street. On my first day there I was taken to the pub by the News Editor and the Assistant News Editor. They said: 'You will drink beer, not shorts, because it's unfair for the boys to have to buy shorts when they're drinking beer. And you will drink half pints rather than pints because a pint looks so ugly in a woman's hand and you will buy your round.'

It seemed very important after all this instruction – and maybe it would have become very important anyway – that I should learn to drink like a gentleman. And that was my aim. I used to drink with the boys, buy my round, and hopefully present a successful drinking image.

There was *a* woman reporter on the staff, as a routine; when I got there, I was the newcomer but I was in *the* woman reporter's role and, although I didn't know what I was doing for the first few months, I had some luck and therefore became the woman reporter. If you were the woman reporter, you were in a good job and got some very nice tasks as a result; some were really fun like limbo dancing in Trafalgar Square.

At that point I was drinking regularly, not all the time, but heavily. Heavily in that between the ages of 21 and 23 I would routinely go to the pub with the boys and drink and it wouldn't be unusual – though it wouldn't be frequent – if I spent all evening drinking with them until either a group of us went off to a restaurant or until the pub closed. I felt it gave me acceptance. I don't know whether I was ex-pected to do this. I think not, but at the time it seemed to me very important that I should drink successfully.

I left that newspaper after about two years and married a journal-ist. He was actually a drunk and this isn't surprising since most of our interactions took place in a pub. He was quite bad, I think, in that re-spect. I lived with him for a year, was married for about two years, and then I left and the marriage was dissolved about two years after that.

At the beginning of the marriage his drinking was much worse than mine. A lot of things were wrong with our marriage, and there was a time when he beat me up quite badly. What is interesting is that not only did I not see my own drinking escalating during this time, but also I didn't see his. That I find odd. When he didn't come home at night I used to think he didn't love me. And when he beat me up I didn't really see the involvement of alcohol. If I'd been sober we wouldn't actually have been at such a pitch of rage with each other that it would have happened in that way (though he has to take the moral responsibility for beating me up). And if I'd ben sober maybe I would have walked out. Drinking does make one vulnerable.

I moved to a nice Sunday newspaper where I met my current husband. We have been very happy. We met 21 years ago but marriage took some time; we weren't in a hurry.

When I left my first husband I had six months when I drank excessively. I knew I did. I would spend all evening in the pub. I was very unhappy because I felt enormous guilt at leaving and a terrible sense of failure. I dealt with my unhappiness with alcohol. It was, I think, during that time that I was in the classic alcoholic/pub-drinking woman's role where I woke up in bed with someone whose name I didn't know. He turned out to be a friend of a friend. I thought this was all very funny but it was the only way to deal with it. I couldn't remember meeting him, couldn't remember going home with him. All I remember is waking up and here was this quite pleasant young man. I can't say I was terribly worried at this point because I had meant to be drunk, I intended to do all this and I didn't care. I didn't care about anything very much.

I became much closer to my present husband, Michael, and we more or less started living together. What's interesting is that after that six months, I reckon I was addicted to alcohol. Before that I may have been. After, I definitely was.

Although I was getting happier and putting my life together again, I couldn't be sure what might happen. Most of the time I was alright, but every six months I would drink more than I meant to. Or behave in a way I wasn't happy with.

I would go to the pub instead of being where I was supposed to be. I think I was hooked, actually. It was work-associated drinking and there was never any question of not going to the pub. At weekends sometimes I drank practically nothing, but during the week there were the first signs of lack of control. I don't think that if you'd looked at me and my fellow drinkers in the pub that you'd have picked me out as the obvious alcoholic by any means because there were people much worse than me.

In that happy newspaper office you worked hard on press day – it was a weekly – but otherwise you went off for long lunches; you had a bottle of wine each at lunch and no-one thought very much of it. And if you did come back too drunk to type, which occasionally happened to me, it wouldn't matter. That would be accepted, assuming it wasn't press day.

I was happily taking part in all that. In the evening we would go to the pub for a few drinks before going home. I'd probably meet Michael in a wine bar. The culture was one of drinking.

On that paper there was a reporter in his sixties who used to be banged up regularly in the police station. Being nice City policemen, the station would ring the editor at home in the early hours of Sunday morning and he would wearily say 'Yes, I will stand bail.' Nobody ever thought that person needed *help*. After I sobered up, I went to the news editor who was a friend of mine and said 'He needs help.' The editor said 'Don't be mean. He's only got a year to go before he retires.' So he never got help, because the news editor saw treatment for alcoholism as shaming and unkind. I tried to explain but it was just pointless.

Some of the people I was having those long lunches with had a great love of drink and some of them had no problem. I still know most of them and some have gone on drinking heavily and falling about and some are fine. Anyway it's all fun and any good party had to have one drunk and one fight, or so it was always said.

Next day you went through all that business about where were you last night? I know there was one time I couldn't remember and I rang up two or three people I'd been with. None of them could remember either and that struck me as very reassuring. One used to re-tell that sort of story and think it was funny.

Within that newspaper my guess is that as many as forty per cent had a drinking problem, certainly in the sections I worked in. And a good twenty per cent had not quite got there yet. I think the traditional female drunk in Fleet Street fiction is there because in actual fact alcohol hits us faster. Also, there is much less acceptance of the drunk woman reporter than there is of the equivalent drunk male. It's unaesthetic for the woman to drink in that way; even though you're meant to stand your round, you're not actually meant to be unladylike.

So there I was doing a job I liked on a newspaper I liked with people I liked, with the man I loved in my life and alcohol was there. My husband was often away on business at that point. While he was there it was fine but when he was away I couldn't be sure what would happen. I might behave well, I might not. Bad behaviour might just mean being helpless so that people had to find me a cab to get home or being obnoxious to the extent of being asked to leave a pub unless I moderated my language. As it was full of effing and blinding journalists anyway I must have been very loud.

There were memory blanks when I just didn't remember. Waking up and thinking 'Where am I?' Opening my eyes cautiously and thinking, phew, thank God I'm at home. And also missing large amounts of money. I suppose I'd drunk it. The business about buying your round had sunk in, so we must have drunk a lot. I used to worry about whether I had been deeply offensive to someone. I was working perfectly adequately and thought to be a hard worker, and indeed I was. Also I found that if I worked very hard I could postpone the drinking. So if I worked until ten at night I could stay out of the pub. One of the mysteries that I still wonder about – only another drunk would understand – is how one would go to the pub at ten and manage to get legless by eleven.

I did have some very bad drinking bouts when my husband was away. Always in company. Having worked on about five or six newspapers I knew lots of people and often used to drink in other newspaper office pubs, so that if I was legless it didn't show in the office so much, or at least that is what I thought.

I went through some of that business of trying to swap the drinks but mostly I didn't bother because I was quite happy to get drunk. My focus was trying to control my behaviour, to avoid too much shame. I tried to drink with people I knew so that with a bit of luck they'd pour me into a cab. I was now starting to get drunk faster which I didn't like. I'd prided myself on being able to drink with the boys but I was often beginning to be drunker than the rest of the company. That I found humiliating. My behaviour was getting madder.

I went to my editor and I said 'I know I'm mad.' Indeed I knew I was not sane. I was paranoid and I thought people were talking behind my back. I knew all that and I said 'Look, this newspaper is driving me mad and I've got to have time off.' He gave me about four months off.

I drank less because I was away from the office and, apart from a really bad drinking binge in the middle, I felt better. I went back to the newspaper. My drinking went even higher than its normal level because all this time it was getting a bit worse. I *was* drinking more, or losing my tolerance or both. I don't know exactly what I drank but I can give an estimate. A normal day – not a heavy drinking day – would start with three quarters of a bottle of wine at lunchtime, five large scotches in the wine bar and then at least another half bottle of wine at home or in a restaurant, probably followed by a couple of scotches. That would be normal drinking, not excessive drinking. That was the routine, days when I felt I hadn't drunk too much, that I considered successful. I didn't drink till lunch, sometimes shaking while I waited and I only drank alone once, in the last week before I stopped drinking. I was always surrounded by people.

On a bad evening I would have had my time in the wine bar and then gone on to another pub, drinking up to ten large scotches until closing time.

I knew we drank too much – I'd written books about health so I knew the facts, but what fun it was! And why not? I even knew that I would probably end up an alcoholic in my fifties because I could see that if I went on like this, drink would probably catch me. I also knew someone who was a nasty drunk. He took one drink and he was vile. It happened in front of my eyes. When he successfully sobered up the second time in the fellowship, I saw the way AA worked (though I thought him very boring when he stopped) and that's very important.

So it was in my mind that if you became an alcoholic you went to Alcoholics Anonymous and I also knew that when you went to AA you had to want to stop altogether. That made perfect sense because I'd been a heavy smoker and I'd stopped, and then started again because I'd taken one cigarette. I'd got the image of addiction in my mind quite clearly well before I thought it applied to me. But I was going mad. That was the bit that really got worse. My behaviour and personality changes were getting odder. At home once, giving a dinner party, I was extremely abusive to a female guest and she walked out. The next morning I couldn't think why I'd done it. It made no sense to me at all. I had various strange theories in my head about why I was going mad.

The missing bit of information for me was the link between alcohol and mental illness. I didn't know that alcoholics were treated in the mental hospitals. I didn't know that it was classified as a mental illness. So when I knew I was heading towards a nervous breakdown (as I saw it) I didn't in any way associate it with alcohol. I didn't have the information to put those two things together. I don't know whether I would have done anyway. I believe that I thought then that alcohol was actually helping me.

After my four months off I went back to work for the newspaper and it all came back again. The drinking was worse. My behaviour really frightened me. I don't know how I didn't get run over or beaten up. I was out of control. I ended up in odd places with bizarre people, people I didn't really like at all and who were not exactly strangers but who were definitely not my friends. I think I almost wanted to be rubbed out. This sounds bizarre but it was a very black life to live. I was full of shame and guilt. I went back to the editor and said 'This newspaper's driving me mad; I'm going to have to leave.' So I left. And at my leaving party (I couldn't remember half of it), I thought 'What have I done?'

My behaviour generally by this time was completely unpredictable – I might be crying in a corner; I might be offering to hit someone; I might be making sexual advances to an old-age pensioner with rheumatism, or I might have been screaming abuse at almost anybody. All these things might have happened and occasionally did. So by now, when I had the blackouts I was absolutely terrified at what I might have done. I didn't know where to get help.

One person helped me – a very drunk Fleet Street reporter. I invited her out to lunch and we drank an immense amount. I said 'My behaviour's very odd', and described to her in graphic detail what was happening to me. She said 'How could you behave like that?' This was from a lady who regularly used to crawl home.

I thought 'Christ! If that's what she thinks of me, I must be really bad.' I have thanked her since. She's still drinking and really, really ill, but her words helped. Another old newspaper friend who knew what I was like had lunch with me and said 'I'm worried about you.' I said 'Oh, I'm having a wonderful time.' He said 'No, I'm worried about you; are you sure you're going to be all right?'

At the time I was writing a story about the Salvation Army who required their officers to sign the pledge not to drink and, although that sounds strange, I had found them very nice people. In contrast my behaviour was really frightening.

I had rung a fellowship of recovering alcoholics when I first got back to work for the newspaper and explained the trouble was I didn't want to stop drinking. They replied, as I thought then pretty unsympathetically, 'Well, come back when you do.' Three months later I rang again and said I was willing to contemplate stopping drinking. The previous evening I really had offended every one of my own personal ethics and I knew that what I was doing was really horrid.

I sat at my desk and I thought 'Well, do I ring the Salvation Army or do I ring my private doctor and get him to recommend a shrink or do I go to AA?' but I thought that it was no good really ringing the Salvation Army because I was not the type. My religious life was not along those lines. I thought about the shrink and decided that really I had a big hatred and fear of them. So I thought 'I'll ring AA.'

I had this moment of clarity when I thought that *maybe* alcohol had something to do with it. I didn't think my weird behaviour would stop, but I thought that if I were not pissed out of my mind, then maybe I could conceal it better. Or if I was going to be abusive, then I wouldn't abuse the only editor who would employ me. That was the most I hoped for, in this moment of truth. It was only a flicker.

I rang AA, had a long chat with a lady and went to my first meeting that morning. I had a terrible hangover. I met someone I knew, a woman I didn't dislike and she later became my sponsor. I have to say I must have concealed my drinking quite well because she thought I was there to do a story. She took me off to have coffee and told me about her life as a drunk, and a bit of it registered. I wouldn't let AA 'Twelve-step' me the formal way because I was too paranoid.

I didn't consider clinic treatment because I didn't know about it or it didn't come into my mind at that moment. I went to a meeting the next day and said I was an alcoholic. I have to say I didn't like AA. I used to go to lunchtime meetings because I didn't want to disrupt my home life.

My husband had been very non-committal. He is a man who leaves people to do their own things. He'd been neither in favour nor against. He may have felt it was something that wouldn't last anyway. I had grave doubts about AA. My third meeting was in the basement of a Catholic church and one of my worst moments was that there was St Ambrose and the Virgin Mary and the Twelve Steps. I thought 'This is just horrifying. This is some sort of Catholic loony meeting. This is really bad news.'

All the talk about God absolutely appalled me. I was a pretty militant atheist. I didn't know whether to trust AA. I heard people say 'If I take another drink, I'll die.' and I thought 'Well that may be true of you but it's not true of me. I'm a middle-class person, I'm not going to die.' Four friends of mine have since died of alcohol. I didn't know much about it then. I thought you died of cirrhosis, I didn't realise that falling downstairs drunk counted as an alcoholic death.

I attended meetings three days a week in London for the first four months and I hated it. Really hated it. The first week hadn't been too bad but I hated all this sweetness and light business.

I was getting angrier and angrier at meetings and eventually I said: 'I can't stick any more of this. This is a fascist organisation. What am I going to do? These people are religious maniacs.' What stayed in my mind, however, was a very nice American who'd been kind to me. I hadn't made much sense but I knew he was being kind and also the idea was that I should try and go to as many meetings as possible. I went to what I'd decided was to be my final meeting.

A very angry man came in and banged on the table and said 'I hate this effing place. I really loathe it. You're sanctimonious prigs but I've got to come here otherwise I'm going to drink because I'm very angry and I've been 18 months off it now and I know I'm going to drink unless I sit in these bloody rooms.' I thought 'Here's one for me. That's it. That's exactly how I feel.' I identified entirely. Up to that point I hadn't.

Fired with this, feeling better, and with the nice little man who was kind to me at the end of the meeting, I thought I'd go to another one and that was a wonderfully deviant AA meeting full of table-thumping atheists and agnostics which had none of the usual set-up. You sat round a table and said what you felt like and asked questions. I banged the table and said 'I'm absolutely fed up with this. It's for re-ligious maniacs, what am I going to do?' And everyone said 'No, no. We're all atheists, don't worry. Just keep going to meetings' and I left that room full of happiness. I thought 'That's great. I can belong to this organisation. And I'll come once a week on Friday afternoons (to what was known as The Fridays Unemployable Meeting) and I'll tell them how awful everybody else is in AA.'

Once I felt I belonged and once I had seen that you can believe what you like, it was different. People say you can believe what you like but you must believe in a Higher Power which is nonsense. You don't have to believe in anything. You just have to turn up.

I emotionally joined AA then. This was after months off drink, in AA. I really liked it then. I started helping at that meeting and funnily enough, once I had been able to tell somebody how angry I felt it was better. I'd been thinking we'd got to be all nice at these meet-ings, feeling you weren't allowed to say you were angry. I had indeed said to one woman 'I feel so angry. Am I allowed to say that at a meet-ing?' and she gave me what I consider very bad advice. She said 'No, no. It's better not to. Sometimes AA members are frightened of anger.' Her reply was nonsense. I'm all for people standing up at meetings cursing us all if they're going to feel better afterwards.

I then went to other meetings. I was absolutely happy from that moment and once I knew it didn't matter, I didn't mind what people said. They could spout on about God as much as they liked because I knew that I could belong and stay a militant atheist if that's what I chose. Also, if someone says I *must* do something, I usually won't; but once I knew it was truly optional I began to be willing to *look* at the steps. Up to that point I'd felt they were compulsory. Then a man at a meeting said he had never done anything but the first step and he was twenty years sober. Once I knew I didn't *have* to do the steps, I became willing to do them.

This man helped hundreds of people including me, selflessly over those twenty years. He was a great person and he may never have paid lip service to the steps but I consider he lived what are the true principles of the steps much better than some of the people who mouthed on about them. He said there were three things that mattered: you have to come to meetings, not drink and do some service. I started doing service – telephone duty. I've done it for the last twelve years and like it very much.

My woman sponsor was unfailingly kind. I was in a state of great guilt and shame and very defiant too. Some people have 'pastry fingers' with people – a light touch – and some people are heavy-handed and not very sensitive to feelings, I needed somebody who was going to be kind.

I found it difficult at home at first because there was alcohol there and I didn't want to throw it away. The 'one day at a time' thing was a help. I tidied it all away in the drinks cupboard.

If Michael was having a drink, he kept it on his side of the table and I drank lots of other things. From the beginning I learned to live alcohol-free while there was alcohol around. This is not true of everybody and some people can't do it. I was lucky and also it did make sense to me because though I might chose to give up drinking, why should anyone else?

As for pubs, I was quite careless to begin with but I became better and didn't go as much because I realised how boring, stressful and tiring they are if you don't drink. So I've done everything wrong in a way, by going to pubs and so on. I was also very suspicious of AA at first, but after that meeting where 'Big Alex' got up and talked I did identify and eventually I did stay out of pubs.

However, I didn't get that miraculous relief some people get immediately. For months I wanted to drink. If I thought about it my mouth would water. I'd have to try and move that thought out with something else.

I now have a lot of friends in AA, some I knew before; there are now a nice lot of hacks – in the days when I first joined there were hardly any. Now I must know ten of the national newspaper journalists in AA. It's really taking off. Practically every newspaper has at least one recovering alcoholic in AA. Perhaps ten years ago there was just one in all.

As to my own work, when I joined AA I'd had two books published – one a mild pornographic novel which contained some of the fantasies of my drinking life and a non-fiction book. When I first stopped drinking I freelanced and started writing a non-fiction book which, from the point of view of attention and reviews, was the best I've ever written. I also did a series of gift books. There's no doubt in my mind that I'm now a faster, better, more competent writer. I'm in control and I'm more of the real me, which is nice. I don't do a lot of rushing-around journalism now and there are aspects of journalism which I find stressful. I do a weekly column for one paper but that's all. Now I just sit around writing books.

As for communicating with the outside world about alcoholism, first of all I wanted to tell the whole world. My sponsor said 'Hang on, keep it quite for a bit. See how you feel after two years.' I decided to keep quiet and it was an awful secret for years until I chose to speak more openly about it. There is a member of my family who has a very bad drinking problem and the other day I went to talk to him in response to a desperate call from neighbours. I talked about my own drinking and found it terribly difficult because within our family the 'let's not talk about it' rule still stands. You can scream and yell about it, but you can't actually *talk* about it.

As for the way I feel about myself now, I am having lots of fun and I do feel well. I compare myself to a woman who was level pegging with me alcohol-wise and I look ten years younger than she, I look ten million times happier than she looks (I don't know how she *feels*), and my career has flourished while hers is declining. All the things that hadn't happened to me have happened to her. She got fired, she's an embarrassment, people look at her at parties and walk to the other end of the room. It is true that if you stop, you become *so* grateful. I used to think 34 was too young to stop. Now I wish I'd stopped at 25. I've had a lot of fun since. I'm happy.

• Lord Mancroft •

◇

Lord Mancroft is a working peer, and lives in London.

I find it difficult to talk honestly about how it was because I don't remember it that well, partly I suppose because it's part of the human condition – and certainly part of the alcoholic condition – to blot out bad things, and partly because thanks to *now*, thanks to AA, it's really quite a long time ago.

Sitting around with using friends (now in recovery) who were there, who were part of it, we'll joke about it, and just occasionally somebody will say something that sends the awful tingle up your spine. God! Remember . . . ! Something that hurts, still hurts. But on the whole, I don't really remember it at all – the feelings, the horror of it – because it has faded very nicely.

I can remember it in factual terms as a nightmare. I can remember the ducking and diving. I can remember the fear and I can remember the rather cold, logical thoughts in the last year of my using. I had come to terms with the fact that I was a junkie, addicted to drugs. I had come to that conclusion. I thought 'Well, how can I live a moderately constructive life as a practising heroin addict?' And after several months and years of trying, I realised that it was impossible. I also knew that I couldn't give up, because I'd tried.

I had never succeeded for any length of time. I always went back to it and I knew that. And so I did have moments of quiet desperation when I logically and coldly thought about it. I remember sitting in my room alone, quietly thinking this thing through, wondering what was the best thing to do. But, of course, in the morning one went off and scored. Went through all that hassle again, so the thoughts were driven from one's mind.

Towards the end, getting high didn't make me high, didn't drive out the feelings; it just made me feel a little bit better. It didn't drive out the sense of desperation – it just left me cold and numb, and very lonely. I wasn't able to explain to anybody how or why I was like this, what I felt about it, or what I was going to do about it.

96

And there was the constant battering I got from people – getting at one, leaning on one to sort one's life out. The extraordinary thing is that (as an analogy) people who drive in London can't park their cars. The general policy now is to make it more difficult to park in London. Nobody thinks back to realise that people don't drive in London for fun. They drive in London because they have to. It seems, therefore, illogical to make it even more difficult.

In a funny sort of way, I feel like that about my using. People used to give me a hard time – people I worked with or my friends and family, constantly day in, day out, battering. Even my dealers, because I never seemed to have enough money, so everyone was getting at me and life was crisis after crisis. I never actually had the courage to stand up and say 'Hang on a minute. I'm not doing this for fun.'

I suppose the answer was at that time I didn't realise what I was doing. I did it because I hadn't got any choice. I didn't know any other way of living and I felt like saying 'This is hurting me just as much as it's hurting you. In fact, more.' I couldn't explain it. And I still find it hard to explain to people that one had lost the choice. One was carried along by events. I just could not stop.

The last thing one wants to do is to hurt one's family. People would ask 'Why do you keep doing this?' You give a pathetic child-like answer, 'I don't know.' The answer is that I did know, but I didn't have the choice. And so the biggest things that recovery has given me is to have the choice. The acceptance of my powerlessness was no problem to me because I had accepted that when I was using. I'm not powerless now in practical terms, because I've taken back the power. As long as I don't use, I've got the power.

The unmanageability is still there. The only difference is now I have the knowledge. I've got the tools. I sometimes use them better than at other times. I'm pretty chaotic. I'm pretty intensive, compulsive, I procrastinate with things I don't like doing. That doesn't change. The only difference now is that I'm probably ten per cent more efficient than I was when I was using. And that ten per cent is the world to me.

Looking back, I can see myself starting to behave in uncomfortable ways – an addict's way of life, starting to feel uncomfortable – I suppose at the age of about eleven. I started not to fit in, to question things that other people didn't question and to react in ways that other children didn't. I can see that now; I couldn't at the time. It seemed to manifest itself over the next few years.

I first had a drink at home at a New Year's Eve party when I was about fourteen and I drank myself clean out. I suppose I did it on purpose and then I started to drink at school. I didn't immediately drink to get drunk the whole time, I often drank more than other people because I thought it made me more relaxed, cool with my friends; it seemed the right thing to do.

That was with my screwed-up alcoholic thinking. I didn't really get into trouble until I started taking drugs, because, like everybody else, I was in a society where it was acceptable to drink. There was no problem getting drink and so it never really created a problem. And indeed that was true of alcohol right up to the end of my using.

Even when I went into treatment, when they asked 'Do you have a problem with alcohol?', I said 'No. I drink too much, but I don't have a problem with it.' That was true. It wasn't a problem for me. And, of course, like most people, I thought my problem was the actual drink and drugs – not the way I felt, not the way I behaved and thought about them.

It was a revelation, when I got sober, that the way I was thinking, behaving, reacting, was wrong. I knew that the superficial behaviour was wrong, but that was because of my drug-taking and my need to acquire drugs. That I understood; what I didn't understand were my compulsions, my emotions, why I felt uncomfortable, why I felt I needed something. I feel I understand it now and I am comfortable with it. I think about it and occasionally I have realisations. Revelations burst upon me.

I feel I'm one of the lucky ones; from the day I stopped using when I went into treatment – not *quite* the day, because I went in kicking and screaming – I grabbed and grasped sobriety with vigour and I've never let it go. I knew when I went into treatment I fought like hell, but when I'd settled down a few days later I looked at the Twelve Steps hanging on the wall and looked at the people around me. After a very short period of time, I realised this worked. I knew, I just knew, that it was right for me.

Looking at my record, my counsellor said I needed more treatment and I knew that it was right for me. I knew how much I wanted it. I knew I wasn't going to screw up. And I didn't. Obviously I didn't understand the full implications of it on Day One.

It was a difficult job to get me there. I went there because I was finally beaten. I used to live like most junkies by stealing enormous amounts of stuff from my family and friends on the basis that they would never do anything about it. I used to sell the family silver at a monotonous pace and they used to go out and buy it back. Finally I stole a piece of jewellery from one of my sisters and instead of the usual screaming, shouting, ranting and raving followed by nothing, she called in the police. I was arrested and charged, not by her but by them. The magistrate, after a bit of engineering behind the scenes, said to me that I could go to treatment or go to prison, so off I went to Hazelden. I got there and I got on an aeroplane and got back home again.

After three days I thought it was a madhouse. I really hated it. I couldn't understand a word they were saying. My parents forced me to go back a week later, so back I went. I realised I was stuck. Couldn't get out of it. So I looked around and started to take it seriously. I was there for six months – in primary care for six weeks and then extended rehabilitation.

I didn't want to go into extended rehab but my visa wouldn't allow me to go into a halfway house and so I thought 'That's it. I'm fine. I want to go home.' Well, I *might* have stayed sober; I don't know. But being able to climb off the bandwagon for six months and just look at oneself and make plans was an amazing opportunity.

I was able to talk it through. For people not on the programme, not alcoholic or in treatment, to be able to go into that much introspection would be wonderful. It was wonderful for me. It was an important thing to do. It hasn't made my life perfect, but it has given me a base, a very solid base from which to work and make my life. And though my life is still full of mistakes and cock-ups – some of which are my fault, some of which are not, things over which I have no control at all – I don't think there now is anything that life can throw at me with which I cannot cope.

There are lots of things life throws at me that I don't like, lots of things that I actively hate, but nothing life throws at me I cannot cope with. That gives me a feeling of great comfort and strength. I know I can get through anything.

One thing I know is not an option (and really this may sound very arrogant, but it really isn't), I know I'm not going to take another drink, or another drug, another pill.

I've often had a feeling that 'One day at a time' can, if you allow it to, become a bit of a cop-out. So I like to qualify it by saying 'One day at a time, for life'. I think if you say 'I'm sober for today (but I might choose to have a drink tomorrow)' it's a cop-out. I say: 'I haven't had a drink today and I'm bloody well not going to have a drink tomorrow.' It's making, for me, a public declaration to myself in the mirror. It's not an option, having a drink. It will never be an option. It doesn't worry me.

The area we cumulatively find the most difficult in sobriety – certainly the one I found the most difficult – is the area of our relationships with the opposite sex, the exclusive relationship. For quite a long time I found it very difficult to form a constructive relationship with someone not on the programme because I was living on one set of rails while they were on a completely different set or no set at all. I couldn't reconcile that at all. I'm going to go on this route – hopefully progressing, though possibly at times regressing – a fixed route and they're not. So, how are we going to marry up, as it were. That was a great problem for me intellectually and I just couldn't resolve it. My counsellor said I had difficulty forming committed relationships. It's not that I had difficulties. I just didn't think they worked.

And yet the idea that one could only form a constructive relationship with someone who's in the programme seemed to me to be very isolating. You can't set out in life saying 'I can only form a relationship with one per cent of women in the world – the other 99 per cent is not going to work.'

As I couldn't reconcile these ideas at all, I went to a 'renewal' at Hazelden about three years ago. We ended up talking for about five or six days about relationships and at the end of it, it dawned on me that I'd never asked the other people in the group what their drug of choice was. It seemed to me to be completely irrelevant. And that I suppose is a definition of sobriety.

As for sensible ordinary people who are not compulsively addicted, they get their lives together. They don't need this childishly simple structure that we have to have. That was the great revelation. They are on a programme but it doesn't have a set of rails. When you met those people *of course* you can form relationships with them. In fact, now that I'm married (I got married seven months ago) the odd thing is that my wife has never seen me other than sober. I was five years sober when I met her.

I choose to say that I'm 'recovered'. 'Recovering' makes it sound as if you've started a course of antibiotics.

I've also got this rather cynical theory that most people are pretty incompetent whether they take drugs or don't. The most important thing – apart from the choice it gives me – is that now I *know* when I'm screwing up and I can live with it, and I know what to do to change it. I'm not wandering around in a fog any more. Now, for me, everything is clear. It doesn't mean to say I don't get lost. There's a difference between the map, which is the way I want to go, and what I actually find on the ground. And it's sometimes difficult to reconcile the two.

But at least I'm not in a fog. I can actually read the signs, without driving into the ditch, and that's very important to me. Like most people I can still live with a certain degree of unmanageability before it gets too bad and I don't mind things going wrong. I can live with that. Fear has gone.

• Ian McShane •

◇

Ian McShane is an actor.
He lives in London and Los Angeles.

I started drinking in my teens, five pints of black and tan, puke it up and start again. That to me was a normal way of drinking. That was how I carried on.

I went to RADA and that's where I really started drinking. I was in a good class. Real actors drank, and that's what we wanted to be. Real actors. There were other actors, who didn't drink, but they weren't the actors I wanted to be. Real actors got drunk.

I don't think I drank because I was shy. I wasn't particularly shy, but I was loath to show off. I never used to jump up at a party and say 'I'll sing you a song'. Now what made me be an actor I don't know. I think it was very much 'Sixties', the new breed. I remember that syndrome of being out there, drinking hard, couldn't wait to do a play because you could get pissed in the evening when you had done the play; you could get round the next day, go for a sauna, stay in there for a few hours so you could get pissed in the morning. Continue. Or you could go there to get ready for the afternoon, go to the theatre, get through the matinee, get through the evening show so you could get pissed again.

I remember that going on for years. It was the same cycle, with films, except you wouldn't drink when you worked. And even then, you did drink when you worked; I remember I said in the first couple of years of sobriety 'I didn't drink when I worked, did I?' And then, when I thought about it, I was half-pissed a lot of the time. How can you not be when you're pissed from the day before. You don't suddenly get sober, just because you've slept for five hours. The booze is still racing around your system.

And sure enough, when you wake up with a hangover, the best cure for it is to have a drink. It works every time. It just means you're pissed again but that's perfectly all right when you're in that mental state. I was like that many times. I think I married the second time out of wanting to do the right thing and settle down. I still think it has something to do with my upbringing which was settled, middle-class, northern, puritanical; there are certain things you don't do, certain things you can do once in a while. I free-based cocaine for one week and then I thought: 'No. I mustn't do that. It's an evil thing.' I'd been doing everything else, but I was drawing a line.

I'd been proud that I never stuck a needle in my arm. I'd stuck a lot of other things up my nose and everywhere else. And what sort of twisted thinking is it that we call somebody who sticks a needle in their arm a junkie? *I* was a junkie. It doesn't matter if there's no needle. That isn't a test. I've snorted, chased round heroin but I've never injected it. That's a real snobbism, an elitism I was putting on it. And from the other side, some say 'You're not a *real* junkie unless you've stuck a needle in yourself. You're not a *real* drug addict.' It's nonsense either way.

In my own case, my life became unmanageable. I had no power over anything, but these are the things you have to go through and you have to learn.

So that was the pattern from the age of eighteen for about 25 years. A pattern of behaviour, of anger, resentment. My personal life came first. Always. My personal desires came before everything else. And my personal destructiveness. At times when I would blame other people, other actors, blame other directors, generally blame *other people* for my lack of success or my anger that I wasn't doing what I thought I should be doing. I know now that was absolute self-indulgence and wilfulness on my own part because I wanted to get pissed, stoned, or whatever. Basically I put that before everything, and then I would complain about what I thought were the real things in my life but I never put them first anyway. My marriage, my career. I didn't care about them. That is typical, self-destructive behaviour.

I would complain about my *real* life but having put my own desires and needs first, I would then blame whatever came out of that evening, or that week, of that using, on my marriage, I couldn't cope, I couldn't do this, I couldn't do that . . . all I, I, I; that came into everything.

I also discovered cocaine in the middle seventies, immediately had a taste and that was it. I was off and running. I found tequila much at the same time. Tequila and cocaine. That was absolute heaven. I took it everywhere, openly in restaurants, just carried it around, laying it out, snorting it off the table. You really thought you were above any kind of restriction.

Not being a user, my wife Gwen would ask why I was doing this. Until I got sober, my behaviour was destroying our relationship.

That's not the real reason I got sober. You get sober for yourself. You can't help anybody else until you've helped yourself. You can't help your relationship until you get sober.

When I met Gwen and I did actually fall in love I think for the first time in my life in a real way, or what turned out to be a real way, I treated her for the first few years like I treated most other things in my life. Things came very easy to me. I'd take her out to dinner and, quite obviously, in the middle of a conversation I'd put a load of cocaine on my hand, snort it up and carry on. She says now 'I should have walked out then.' And I say 'But you didn't.' She changed but I didn't change for a few years. I was still thinking I could carry on using. I think it became a lot less appealing to me later on when the whole thing turned round on me in a very bad and sad way.

I didn't get high any more. I got low all the time. I'd come home after working and would stay up after Gwen had gone to bed, saying I was doing a crossword puzzle. I had the vodka or the tequila iced in the fridge, I'd line up a crossword, I'd get out the coke, I'd get out the joints but I wouldn't get out the alcohol because I liked that walk to the fridge.

So I'd lay out the line of coke and snort it and put out the crossword, then I'd get out the drink and take a swig, back in the freezer, and come back and smoke a slow joint. By the time I'd done that, I was so blasted with the joint I was ready to do another line of coke. And the cycle ... by the time this had happened, I'd not looked at the crossword. This was simply the wonderful excuse. By this time I couldn't *see* Seven Across, never mind *do* it. It was just an excuse to get loaded.

This would start around midnight and it would go on until three in the morning; I'd be a gibbering idiot. I'd go to bed and lie there with the awful feeling of lying next to someone who knows what you've been doing and knows they can't do anything to help. You know you're a liar and a cheat and a thief of time, and a thief of everything else, but yet have to go on and on doing it.

For me that went on for another two years before it really came to an end. I was sneaking. I was trying to tell Gwen I wasn't doing it. I'd reached the stage where she *knew* I did drugs, and then I started to lie about them. That's terrible when you just lie to somebody you love about it constantly. One day in early 1988, Gwen went out in the afternoon and I immediately got the port out. I did two grammes of cocaine and a lot of port. I was completely smashed.

I remembered I had talked with another actor a few months before about sobriety because I'd been feeling this on and off. But I'd never done anything more than a token gesture towards sobriety. I'd never gone to a meeting. I'd only ever taken it in my own hands because, of course, I was omnipotent and could do everything.

I'd only ever stopped doing cocaine for a month but carried on with cannabis, and I'd give up cannabis and go back to cocaine because wasn't I being good giving up one and then the other. All the time I was taking in uppers and downers and 'ludes' and speed as part of a life support – and smoking cigarettes and drinking vodka as a standby.

Also, I think you look at yourself. Well, I *couldn't* look at myself then, not much, because I was scared at the way I was starting to look. It wasn't looking like me any more.

On this day I'd taken a lot of coke and a lot of port and an urge came on ... 'This is fucking ridiculous.' It was a now-or-never urge for help and I called Bobby N. in LA and said 'What do I do?' He replied 'Go to a meeting.' I pleaded ignorance and said 'Oh sure.' I put the phone down and phoned him back and said 'I don't know a meeting ...' Obviously I was saying I needed somebody to take me. And he did. He simply told me to be outside my house at a quarter to seven. My wife arrived back around twenty to seven and I said 'I'm just out the door'. I had a shower and I thought I was sober. When asked where I was going I said 'I'm just going to a meeting. I don't like my life any more.' And I left. I just brushed past her. I said 'I love you' and I left.

Bobby N. was waiting outside and took me to a meeting in Melrose. I don't remember much about it. There was a lot of jabbering. All he said to me was 'You sit here. You don't have to say anything. If they ask you if you're an alcoholic, you don't even have to get up and say you're an alcoholic. Just listen and see if anything clicks.' So I sat there. I don't think anything clicked except I liked him and I knew what sobriety he had. I asked 'How long he had been coming to these meetings. He said he hadn't used and he hadn't drunk for eight or nine years. I liked him. I'd heard his name in other ways not connected with sobriety or anything like that. I saw one or two other people there and I don't think anything did click at that *meeting* but the *people* there did it and *he* did it.

He took me home, came in for a coffee, sat down. He said: 'Be good to yourself. Just go to a meeting tomorrow. Try and go to ninety meetings in ninety days; you'll get all the literature tomorrow. If you feel restless, light a candle, go and have a nice warm bath, play soothing music, have a cup of tea, put a nice towelling gown on, do nice things for yourself, don't feel pressured. And don't pick up a drink.'

And I didn't. The next day I went to a meeting. I just zapped out to the first meeting in the morning, at twelve. I'm a wonderful procrastinator at the best of times; I'd never tried this before. Whether it was something inside me saying 'I'll be letting him down' or letting myself down I don't know. There's nothing wrong in that; maybe the first few meetings I went to because I didn't want to let Bobby down and that was the best feeling in the world.

I wasn't sure if I wanted to go, but I didn't care. I went to meetings. That lunchtime meeting turned out to be a gay non-smoking meeting. I didn't know. I sat there and these gay guys talked about sexual problems. I thought: 'Well, I don't understand, but there'll be another meeting.' There's a meeting on every corner in Los Angeles.

I then found the crack meeting in the local Log Cabin which has been going for a long time, and I was there most mornings at seven-thirty. I would also go to the lunch-time one. There were funny meetings like Artists in Sobriety which I thought a bit pretentious, a great name but it doesn't matter, because you can't blame the meetings. We all know that.

So I did the ninety meetings in ninety days. I'd had coke nightmares, waking up swearing I'd done coke; I'd get up and read that Alcoholics Anonymous book and sure enough, it would send me straight to sleep sometimes, but I just did what it said.

I think in the first few weeks that certain people I saw were classic old-timers whom I listened to. They said the same old thing, 'Don't pick up that drink. You don't *have* to find your Higher Power. You may never find a Higher Power, but don't pick up that drink. Don't make any promises. Just for today. Let go, let God. Easy does it.'

All those slogans work. There are no medals in this, no diploma at the end of this, you don't get a certificate saying 'I'm sober' because it could change. It's always there. There's always a drink whenever you want it.

Sobriety is a big deal and it's the best deal in town. It really is. From sobriety, from those first few weeks when I didn't know what was happening, I didn't have a clue what was going on, but I *did* know that what was happening to me was better than anything that had happened in a while. *I wasn't drinking.* It was as simple as that.

I'll never forget one meeting I went to. An old guy said something very strange. He said 'Your eye finally got back into shape, your eye finally went back OK.' I said 'Pardon?' He said 'Well your eye was really, sort of wild'. He wasn't being funny; I thought he was taking the mickey but he wasn't. It was that crazy look, and obviously he'd seen it. He said 'Well, you're looking better.' I could have chinned the guy but I said 'Thank you.' He wasn't saying anything funny. People say things in the fellowship to help. You're there to help each other.

That first few months were very exciting, very scary; all I knew was that I wanted to get some time in very quickly. I asked all the classic questions, like 'Will I be sober tomorrow; will I make it?' Sometimes it was 'Will I get through *today*?' The thoughts of 'I must have a drink' or 'I must have a line of coke' went very quickly. But the classic thoughts of 'Will I never have one again; how long is this for?' were around for a while and then gradually through taking action (which is the only way to deal with it – by speaking to people, by going to meetings) those thoughts went.

I didn't see anyone with whom I did drugs, even those who were great friends. I've discovered there are certain people I don't see any more, not because I don't like them, but because I simply drank with them. I used with them. I don't do that any more so I never see them. They're still doing it; I'd be a drag on them and they'd certainly be a drag to me.

And pubs! I don't mind going into a bar to meet someone, but I don't spend time there. After fifteen or twenty minutes, it gets tedious. I used to sit there and recycle the same old rubbish, change the world, but not anymore.

All those things I used to do, promising Gwen 'I'm coming in tonight. I'm only going to have five large vodkas.' This is at seven-thirty. By a quarter to eight I've already increased it to seven large vodkas. And then the amounts and the time change as the evening goes on. By eight-thirty I'm pissed. By ten o'clock I'm thinking the bitch shouldn't try and fuck me about. How dare she put these re-strictions on me. I'm a fucking good man. I'll show her! I won't go home till two in the morning . . .' Great thinking.

I can think about that now and smile about it. It didn't happen *every* night but it happened often enough. It's not funny in the end. You walk in finally and you're making excuses for yourself: 'The reason I'm late is because you make me stay out. And you're lucky I'm coming home anyway. I'm coming home just to see you. I could really be out having a good time.'

What is this craziness? What is this madness? Now and again my wife says 'Your halo's slipping, it's tarnishing a little, love. You'll have to polish it.' I laugh. But I am a better person, though I never was a shit, basically. My craziness was drug-induced. I was trying to be something else. Something you learn, I think, through this fellow-ship is about what kind of person you are. Some people may never 'get it'. I'm among the lucky ones. Going to that meeting is the best thing I've ever done. Gwen and I have now been married for 12 years.

I'm reminded constantly about meetings. Sometimes I'm working and can't make a meeting but there's always the phone. Wherever you want to be the fellowship's there, but the meetings are important to get back to because that's where it started. That's where you have one drunk talking to another and that's what it's about. Someone once said to me 'Once you've been in the fellowship – for any amount of time at all, if you go out there and drink and have a belly full of alcohol and a head full of the fellowship, it must be the most deadly combination.' I'm not surprised that people say when they go out and drink that they go back into a hell which is worse than before they came in.

The disease *does* become progressive. Really I don't think I want to find out about that. I'm not curious to see what a slip would be like. Again, it's not smugness, but it's like saying that *would* be greedy. A couple of drinks, anyway, doesn't mean anything. It never did. I never drank for the taste pleasure. When people talk about this red wine, you can taste the blackberry with a slight hint of the apricot', I think 'I liked *alcohol*'. Down the throat, hard as you can, hits you there and gets you where you want to be very quickly. Zap. Like coke madness. After the first time you've done that, you're then chasing that one first hit for the rest of your life. Or with alcohol you're chasing that first flush.

There are people who order one glass of wine, sip it for an hour and then order another one. They have two glasses of wine over two and a half hours. That's normal. Normal people actually do that. Many millions and millions of people do that. The majority.

· NELL ·

Nell is a researcher and lives in London.

I drank for twenty years. Looking back now I was almost certainly drinking alcoholically for the last ten of those years; and I was drinking for oblivion for the last three years.

My parents didn't drink every day but booze was in the house, and from the age of around fifteen we were encouraged to drink. Even from that age I was always greedy for drink. I always wanted another glass. I always wanted to open another bottle. I was always worried there wasn't going to be enough. We used to have evenings when we'd all get drunk and sing.

At the age of nineteen I moved into a flat with some girls. I didn't drink there because I couldn't afford it. But if I went anywhere or did anything, drink was always around and I can see now that I didn't really do anything that wasn't connected with drink. Even when I went to the cinema, I left before the end of the film to get to the pub. Drink was very much a part of my life.

When I started to work, I was in environments where drink was available and I worked with drinkers. I can seen now that I chose that. I was comfortable with that environment, with people who drank a lot. I always had the most enormous capacity for alcohol. In fact, when I got into the fellowship, one thing my father kept telling me was 'You can't be an alcoholic; you used to drink me under the table.' I used to pride myself on the amount I drank and I'd go into the pub and match people pint for pint or double for double. It was always doubles.

From a very early age, as far back as I can remember, I've always been fearful and I lived a lot of my life thinking I was going to be found out – I never quite knew what it was that I'd done. I think it was really *who* I was that was going to be found out. The more I went on through life and the more I drank, the more fearful I became. I drank progressively more and more. At work there were people who drank at lunchtime, people who drank in the afternoons and people who drank in the evenings and slowly I ended up drinking with all of them. The pubs weren't open in the afternoon then but there were clubs and I always thought them risqué, fun and grown-up.

Underneath all this, I was getting more and more unhappy. Never happy where I was, always striving for something to make me happier. I did a lot of moving around, changed countries, changed jobs, changed flats, boyfriends. To begin with, I thought I was going to be happy but I was striving for something, constantly looking for the knight in shining armour. I really expected that something or someone was going to rescue me. I relied a lot on people to make it all happen and of course they never did. I had three periods when I got amazingly depressed. I see now that they were caused by three very heavy binges of drinking vast quantities on top of my regular daily drinking.

I went to a doctor who smoked and who had one of those big pub ashtrays – that's why I chose him – and he told me I had a chemical imbalance of the brain (quite right of course) and I should 'take these pills'. There were certain foods I couldn't eat with them, but you could drink with them!

So I carried on drinking, just daily 'normal' drinking, not binge-drinking, thinking I was all right. I suppose these three occasions had been over a period of five or six years. The last time I went to see the doctor I had been so terrified I had to get someone to take me. I was incapable of getting there on my own.

It never occurred to me then that I had a problem with booze. It was ten years before I finally stopped drinking. And so I carried on, changing jobs, flats, boyfriends, taking extended holidays. Very slowly the quality of my life was deteriorating. I pretended it wasn't. I went to France, the Middle East, Australia, but I might as well have been in Brighton. One of the great regrets of my life is that I wasn't able to appreciate my surroundings. I could have been anywhere.

I was still being offered work. Looking back now I can see that I was never, ever, promoted. I always had to move. I was never fired. I always had to move because things weren't right. So about every two years I changed jobs thinking it might be better elsewhere. I certainly didn't make any wise career moves.

I just went where I was offered a job. I was able to find the drinkers where I worked; that became a factor, *drinking and working*, so the jobs I was getting tended to be getting further down the scale. I was getting more and more aggressive. It became the only way I knew of keeping things together. I have dreadful memories of screaming at people because it was the only way I knew to command any attention. I didn't know how to get things done by asking people nicely.

I didn't know that any of this was booze. I thought it was me. I could see other people laughing and getting on with their lives. I felt there was something wrong with me. I didn't know how to do what other people did. It wasn't in my experience to do things the right way. I had never learned to see anything from the other's point of view or how to ask anyone to do anything with love or kindness. It was just 'I want, now; do!'

Eventually I lived with a man whom I thought was going to rescue me. He died very suddenly and for a long time I thought his death was a cause of my drinking. I couldn't see anything beyond his dying, to see that by the time we met I already had a real problem with booze. For some reason, when I met him, being with him was more powerful than drinking. I controlled my drinking. I didn't drink in the mornings; I used to go home and cook. We did things together.

Very slowly the drinking crept back in, and I was doing things that I was very ashamed of. I was with a man who was supposed to be wonderful and here I was waiting for him to go to work so I could have a large vodka before I could go into work. I didn't know why it happened and we'd end up having rows. He used to ask 'How is it you suddenly change? I don't understand it.' Neither did I. When he died, the only thing I knew to do was drink. People suggested I get pills from the doctor but I said I would stick to drink because pills would lead to addiction . . . I would drink for three weeks! I couldn't stop and was drinking round the clock.

After about three months of that, I went back to work somehow. God knows how they put up with me. I went to Australia, not drinking, for a month at Christmas and when I came back it was like walking into a wall of despair. Straight back into really heavy drinking and trying to work. A friend suggested a doctor who prescribed me the tranquiliser Ativan on condition I went for counselling.

I went for counselling and took the Ativan. Then I started drinking again. I found a chemist who would renew my prescription. From counselling sessions – where I used to cry for an hour – I went straight to the pub, and then back home for more booze. *Nobody mentioned that I shouldn't drink.*

I didn't deal with my feelings. When Richard died it was instant despair and because I didn't confront the despair, it kept repeating. When my mother died it was a double dose of misery and that was the beginning of my stopping work and doing nothing but feel sorry for myself and drink.

I really didn't do anything for a year. Didn't eat, didn't go out, didn't see anyone, nor talk on the telephone. I didn't look after myself in any way. I never cleaned. I had a cleaner who came in and all she did was clear up the glasses, wash them and put them away and hoover. I wasn't working but I had been left some money and I was living on that.

Eventually, my sister – on whom I was heavily dependent – came and got me and I ended up in a treatment centre. She said 'You are killing yourself. You cannot do this any longer. If *you* don't care about yourself, I do.'

Before going into treatment I stayed with her and there was an agreement that I would be allowed two drinks a day. Almost from the start I cheated, working through their drinks cupboard from the back to the front; my last drink was Cointreau with lemon squash. When I went out to get cigarettes I would spend four hours in the pub, so eventually I agreed to go to the treatment centre. I thought it was going to be a cross between a nursing home and a hotel. I thought they were going to be nice to me. Instead of which, I discovered that I had to start looking at myself and talking about myself, and that I had to give some kind of input into this thing they called 'recovery.'

The centre was run on AA lines with the Twelve Steps. I found it hard to let go and tell people how I felt because for years I had avoided doing that. After about four weeks of avoiding talking about feelings, trying to blend in with the wallpaper, they told me that if I didn't start working they'd throw me out. That terrified me.

I started to talk about myself. I began to look at *my* part in things. I found it hard but I didn't find it terrifying; it was a relief in some ways. I remember a fellowship meeting with a man doing the 'chair' and I couldn't believe that anyone could be so honest. I cried all the way through and afterwards I went up to him and said 'I want to be like you. I want to be able to talk the way you talk.' That was the beginning of me wanting to get well.

When I left treatment they said they could only give me the tools; if I wanted to stay away from drink a day at a time, then I'd have to go to meetings of the fellowship. That was the only method that worked. I wasn't at all sure about that. I was desperately worried about my social life!

However my social life by the time I got to treatment consisted of me sitting in front of a television set or listening to sad songs, crying. That was my social life. I had stopped going to the pub. I couldn't walk by the time I got to treatment. I could only shuffle along, I couldn't manage steps.

I looked dreadful. I was two stone heavier than I am now – I'm not tall – totally bloated and I wore really baggy clothes. I didn't wash, didn't have a bath for months on end (I couldn't cope with getting into a bath), didn't wash my hair, didn't iron clothes. I didn't wear make-up, and couldn't cut my nails. I couldn't see how I was. I used to go everywhere in this state, reeking of alcohol, peppermints and Arpège.

I left treatment, worried about 'having to go to meetings', worried about social life and so on. I did go to meetings because I didn't want to drink and I had nowhere else to go. By this time I was more frightened of drinking again than I was of anything else. That was a really big fear for me.

Very soon, in the first meeting I think, I liked the fellowship, liked the people. I shared and then began to go to meetings. I got to know people and made a few chums in the fellowship. In fact, they now were the only people I knew. Very early on I got a sponsor. I got to love AA – the laughter, the honesty and particularly that, after being in treatment for three months where you had daily commitments to share, in AA I could share when I wanted to. That is to say I could share because I identified, because I understood, and not because I had to share that particular Wednesday afternoon.

I had thought that meetings of the fellowship would be very boring, full of do-gooders; that it would be no fun, without humour, a matter of just sitting around and being really heavy about drinking. Of course, they were nothing like that. They were great.

After about a year I started to go to Step Meetings (meetings where one at a time, the Twelve Steps suggested by AA as a programme of recovery are discussed) and that was when I started to understand about progress, that it was more than about drinking, that it was about changing *me* and my attitudes. I heard somewhere along the way that AA for instance stood for altered attitudes and at this time I could see that I had to alter a lot of my thinking if I was to have any kind of real happiness, any real long-term recovery. I started 'working the steps' and for me now the steps are just such an important factor in my life. They *are* the programme. It's now not enough for me not to drink, a day at a time (although that's always bottom line), it's also important to progress emotionally and spiritually.

It's about a year since I did step three, about handing my will and life over to the care of God, *as I understand Him*. That was very important, making a commitment to a power that I'd come to believe in. I've needed that power as I've gone on. As a result I have been able to change my attitudes. I had been a very fearful person with exceedingly low self-esteem. Any courage or 'front' had come from the bottle or from hiding behind other people. Any joy I'd got had come from the bottle. I didn't know how to stand up on my own as a person. And be counted.

The more I got into the steps, the more I could see that if I followed the steps and tried to practise the programme in my life (as in the twelfth step) I could change into a person who could cope with life. I could become a person who wasn't afraid. I didn't want to find a way of *avoiding* the fear, but rather a way of removing the fear so that it wasn't there in the first place. I would become a person who could replace fear with something else so I could live my life from love, if you like.

And that's what been happening to me in the last five years. Very slowly, because everything for me is very slow. It takes a lot of time for me to get insight on board; I realised when I was talking about being enlightened that what that meant was letting the light in. I hadn't twigged.

So, going through my life doing the steps, step by step, it's all finding out about me, the sort of person I am. A lot of it is discovering first the person I *became*, through drink and before that, through fearful behaviour. Though working this programme I am sifting through that rubbish. A lot of it is very painful but I know that I am given the courage to go back through it.

Whenever I ask the Higher Power for anything, any help of any kind, I am given help from God or from other people. It happens in waves. It's not like a car going straight, it's more like something at sea, I go forward a bit, then I go back a bit. I go forward a bit more and so it goes on, making progress. Things happen in my life that force me to look at myself and bring about a change because I am the only person I can change. I've tried all that other stuff about changing other people. I've tried running away. It doesn't work.

Unless I deal with things, they keep coming up wearing different hats. Just lately I've been forced to see in a really big way how I've never known how to love. Never known how to give love, nor how to receive love. And I'm learning now. I've been going through the barrier of not being able to love. And I'm finding that the more I can love, the less I fear. I'm now making a conscious daily effort to be a loving person. I have to practise in the morning when I get up through conscious contact with God and at night. The more I practise the easier it becomes, and the happier I am. And therefore it is not a chore at all. There are rewards. It's living my life from a different viewpoint. It's turning it round.

I find also that I'm in a new sense of time. Some things I learned last week feel as if I've known them all my life and some things I knew three years ago seem as if I only learned them yesterday. My sense of time has completely altered.

When I got sober I couldn't work. I was incapable of work. After about six months I went to the local employment agency and a sweet girl in there let me practise on her typewriter. I hadn't typed for years. I went out and became a copy-typist.

I did a lot of freelancing because freelancing means that you don't have to get to know people. I've been with my present company for over a year working with the same people; and two weeks ago I moved – the job moved into its next phase and I moved with it. I'm now working with five people I didn't know before, five people I wasn't at all sure about. All my old fears of inadequacy and conflict came up, particularly concerning one person of whom I had a lot of fear. I was very conscious that I had to change. This person wasn't going to change and I had to learn to accept this. I wanted him to be a different person, different accent, different shape, different human being really. I wanted him to understand me. I didn't even think that *I* might try to understand *him*. I could judge him, but I couldn't actually understand him or love him in any way.

I did a lot of talking about it. In fact I did a chair about it the night before I came to the new job. I told everybody how fearful I was. *That's the beauty of the fellowship for me: I can talk about how I feel.* And there's some magic formula that says that if I can share anything – and now I've got to the point where I can share anything – I *can* be well and that it's more important for me to be well than to care about what people are thinking of me. It's taken me a while to get there.

If I share something, the problem is immediately halved. I'm no longer in fear of it. In the chair I talked about this man and how I was in fear of him, how I was worried and how I've been judging him, how I've been trying to separate myself from this person and the new people I was going to be working with, trying to make that little separate identity. I realised that if I was going to work with a team and we were (or I was) going to be happy, instead of separating myself I was going to have to integrate myself.

It was during the time I was working consciously on how to *love* that I began the job and it's wonderful now. Every morning when I come to work I skip in. I'm pleased to see these people. I really like them and I'm not judging them. As for the man in particular, I can actually now say to him 'Can you give me a hug?' That is a total turn-around. Loving him as a total being and seeing that his aggression, which I'd feared, was merely a cloak for *his* fear.

So thanks to the programme, that is dealt with. I'm now stopping smoking on a Twelve Step programme and it really is now far more than just not drinking, though that will always be the bottom line.

One day at a time.

· MOLLY PARKIN ·

◇

*Molly Parkin is an artist and writer who lives
in London and Cornwall.*

I come from a teetotal background, Welsh Chapel. My granny had
suffered at the hands of alcoholism in her own family. Drink was
absolutely forbidden and in childhood we were trained to walk on
the other side of the road from the pub. Immediately it became
rather fascinating because drink was so outside the pale, especially
for women.

So my childhood didn't have alcohol in it, except by reference.
Then it was thought to be the greatest sin. I loved life in the Chapel,
but my parents moved from that mining valley to London to seek
their fortune. From what I understand now, in my father's life, alcohol reared its head quite early on, but he restrained himself and it
was not in our upbringing. No alcohol at all.

I was completely teetotal until I became an art student in London. I
then moved to Brighton with my parents, which was for them the
worst possible move because there they discovered Merrydown
Cider. That was my first taste of being in a pub and I hated it. I didn't
like the effect of the cider on me or my parents. I vowed never to be
like that.

But, when I came to London after college, my first drink was in the
Studio Club in Swallow Street. I was with a girlfriend and I said 'What
do I ask for when these men ask me what I want to drink?' and she
said 'Large gin and Dubonnet.' She said it very firmly. 'A double, you
ask for. A single's no good to anybody.'

And that's what I asked for, sitting on a bar-stool. I hated the taste
but loved the effect. It immediately changed me from a prim Welsh
chapel puritan girl into the Vamp of the Valleys. I had a complete
personality change, immediately. I knew it was for me and I never
looked back. I was 21 or 22, and I'd waited all that time for that drink.

I loved what that drink did for me. There was no stopping. I'd
known that compulsive side of me from chocolates and from an
addiction to work. So when the drink turned up, it completed the

117

circle because it gave me a sense of being able to function in company. I was desperately shy, and rather played along with that shy look. I felt extremely over-sensitive and self-conscious in a group. I couldn't easily talk without feeling I wanted the earth to swallow me up and I certainly couldn't cope with attention from the opposite sex. I never found that easy. I found it excruciating.

I'd always felt out of kilter from the very beginning, as if I'd got one skin less than everybody else. And the drink gave me the extra skin. It simply was my best friend for about twenty-five years until it started to be my worst enemy, and in the end it was an evil predator. Rapacious.

In my youth I only drank in the evenings but I did it every evening. I was teaching at the Elephant and Castle. I had the classic alcoholic's split existence. I was devoted to teaching impoverished children in the daytime (and getting amazing work out of them) but then I would don another mantle for the evening.

I would go to nightclubs and spend time with people like Christine Keeler. I didn't meet Profumo and Lord Astor, but I met other people like that and my evenings were spent in extremely wealthy situations. I was the fresh young thing who would pass out at a certain point and I did that deliberately. I didn't want to know what they were going to get up to with my nubile young body but I liked being where it was awash with champagne and if I'd stayed with the people I was teaching, the money simply wasn't there to satisfy my thirst.

This was, in the evenings, 'the fast set' of the 1950s; they were astonished I had to get up in the mornings, to get to the Elephant and Castle when I was waking up in Belgravia. I loved doing my work and I excelled in my job because alcoholics are achievers. One life wouldn't have been sufficient without the other. I needed the contrast and the alcohol fuelled this sense of disorientation from having to change from a Goodtime Girl by night to Salvation Army creature by day.

At college I hadn't been a drinker at all. I had become highly qualified. I went to art school for five years and won travelling scholarships to Italy. That was what I thought my life would be.

But it wasn't. In London, hangovers became an instant way of life. I never *didn't* have a hangover. They were excruciating from the very beginning. I had to have West End night clubs every evening, and sex was mixed up in it.

I chose alcoholic men. The only man in my life who wasn't alcoholic was my first fiancé whom I didn't marry because my alcoholic father put an end to it. (I was reunited with that fiancé last year.) I was inundated with men because I behaved in a particularly flirtatious way, a seductive manner picked up from Hollywood of course. And all the men were alcoholics.

I'd always loved those films where there were night club scenes where champagne was popping. It seemed to me that I had it made. I was Rita Hayworth.

I loved my work in the Elephant and Castle and I loved being with all these men like Onassis and all of that lot because they seemed to have the answer. I'd liked it best at my grandfather's; I felt most comfortable with older men. They knew what they were doing. They had a lifestyle which I wanted.

I wasn't interested in being with young men where you had to wait at the bus-stop. My impatience wouldn't have allowed me to do that. It was taxis and Rolls Royces and that was how my life was. Young men couldn't buy you champagne and fete you and give you pretty clothes.

My father died. I finished my relationship with an older man because he reminded me of my father and I met the young man whom I married. We were both drunk when we met at a party. We each drank as much as the other. He asked me to marry him on the second date. I said yes. I didn't know him at all. He was with the Forces and we went to live in Germany.

And that was real, heavy drinking. I drank solidly; whisky. He was an Oxford MA, everything my family required so for me it was *big* people pleasing, seeking approval; exactly what the doctor ordered.

We had a very posh London wedding in Lowndes Square, the house of one of my sugar daddies who'd provided it as a present. All up and over the top. I was completely out of my depth and had started to assume a posh Rodean accent which wasn't me at all and which was terrifying after a few drinks. I had to speak very slowly so I didn't drop aitchs and all of that.

Now I was a different person and the alcohol built my self-confidence because the fear was overwhelming and I was out of my depth socially, spending weekends in castles and country houses. We were shooting and fishing and there wasn't anybody I could relate to – not even my husband. In time we had two small children. I started to experience enormous success with painting, doing it every day. I sold a lot.

When we divorced, I went into journalism. My first job was on Nova. I moved to Harper's and then the Sunday Times and it was there more than at the magazines that my art just disappeared overnight. I became fashion editor and my muse vanished. I had the most appalling and disastrous creative block as a painter. After being so prolific I simply couldn't paint at all. Whether it was the alcohol which stopped my muse or whether it was the trauma of the divorce and being alone with two small girls, I don't know.

I went into fashion. I started designing hats and bags for Biba and roistering around in the night. And then I opened my own boutique.

I was in dreadful pain over the end of my marriage and that started a different persona. I became strident. I returned to a working-class accent and I felt totally at home with the people among whom I was now moving: people like David Bailey, Duffy and Terry Donovan, the three cockney photographers. We went to night clubs like the Ad Lib. People like the Beatles and the Rolling Stones went there so I was in tune with the times. Perfect timing, perfect drinking. I loved being in those discos every night. I had become fashion editor of Nova – the right magazine at the right time – and started having business lunches and began drinking at lunchtime. And that became much worse.

I started on television with an outrageous persona. I was pissed half the time so I didn't know what I was doing. But so was everybody else – it was the spirit of the times.

I had plenty of money and my own yellow Rolls Royce 1932 vintage; I had my yellow house in Old Church Street and the yellow Morgan as well and it was all show, show, show. But inside I was just withering away. Nobody could have known. But I knew. It was daily drinking and twice daily hangovers. On the Sunday Times we would all go to the pub opposite the office to do our page. And then in the afternoon there'd be a hangover, until half past five and I just couldn't wait to get a drink. By this time I'd got married a second time to Patrick, who was an artist and I had to disguise my hangover because he thought that when we met for a drink in the evening – for which he was as eager as I was – it was my first drink. We'd really whack into it. We had an intensely social life. Our house was open house with huge parties surrounded by people who drank as heavily as ourselves.

I simply didn't know anybody who didn't drink. Nor would I have been in that situation if I hadn't drunk. Everyone was successful. Everyone was into everything. (I didn't do drugs at that time.)

And then I left the Sunday Times. I was sacked from other journalistic jobs too and I'd think 'Oh God. I've done it again.' It was only for a moment. I didn't have any job to go to, so alcohol fuelled the bravado. These jobs meant nothing to me. *I was a painter*.

I was meant to be painting. That's what I wanted my life to be. And here I was doing what I really scorned. I really hated what I'd become, this loud-mouthed, outrageous fashion editor. It was so puerile. *I was a painter*.

We moved to Cornwall and the drinking took on a different colour again. We didn't drink at all during the week but then at the weekend it became binge-drinking. On Friday night we'd play darts with all the artists, starting the drinking. We'd go to deserted beaches, a whole horde of us, and because we were drinking in the open air, diving into the ocean and playing beach cricket, it didn't feel like drinking. We would take whole crates with us. It was the drinking that was the point of everything. Sunday night used to be different because we were trying not to have a drink, to sober up for Monday morning.

That was when there were ten novels in ten years and a lot of journalism. So I hadn't stopped working; drink hadn't eroded that yet. But it was to do so. For now, everything I touched turned to gold. I was a best-selling authoress.

In Cornwall we lived on the side of a cliff, with our own electricity supplied by windmill. The rustic life, but it didn't really change us. Berry Bros and Rudd of St James' said they'd deliver wine anywhere in England which meant then that you'd have to put in a hefty order to make it worth their while. We were nearly at Land's End so we put in huge orders and got into wine in a big way.

We thought if we had a really *nice* bottle of wine we wouldn't drink as much, so we had to have sherry before a meal and then after two sherries we were already at each other's throats. It made us very, very aggressive. By the time we would eat the gourmet meal that I'd prepared and drunk the gourmet's claret, we were at it, quarrelling. Already I think that marriage was suffering from the effects of alcohol.

It really took off when, in the late 1970s we went to live in New York. It took an absolute dive. Everything happened. We lost our moral fibre in New York. We went to live in the Chelsea Hotel, the bastion of Bohemian depravity and got into drugs in a serious way. I was still working. And so was he. That hadn't disappeared but we had strange hours, going to bed at five o'clock in the evening and working at half-past ten, eleven at night and then preparing ourselves for going out to Club 54 where you were only let in if you looked all right. We would have worked all day, swum for an hour at the Y and eaten vegetarian, so in that sense we appeared to be taking care of ourselves, of our bodies except that we weren't.

We were completely out of touch with reality. I was in and out of hallucinations and Patrick said I was to stop smoking dope because he was frightened of the images I was conjuring up. He thought I was going to end up like my mother. She had been in and out of mental homes.

We were using drink and cocaine, spending all night in the clubs until seven in the morning. We'd go to the Empire Diner round the corner from the Chelsea for breakfast where I would have a bloody Mary. I didn't like it if Patrick had it without vodka because it felt like a criticism of me.

People were just dying in our circle. OD'ing. It seemed like 'Oh, yeah . . . Where's so and so?' 'OD'd' 'Oh, right. What are we doing tonight?' That was New York, for a year. We went there in 1979 and we came back in 1980.

My little mother was the saving of me because she started going into senility. We came home. Within a fortnight of our return our marriage simply couldn't be sustained. Patrick and I split up.

I was writing one of my final novels, with immense difficulty. I had run out of imagination and ingenuity and all I cold do was take events in my life and put them down on paper. I had a final 18-month fling in London which was just nightmarish. I was totally out of control. Manic. Drinking then became all the time. That's when it became 'in the morning drinking'. I wrote a film and a play with incredible difficulty. I was in real trouble and I didn't know what to do. I didn't know anyone who'd been in a treatment centre and I didn't know anyone who'd given up drinking.

But I was to hit a further rock bottom than that. I was now in total misery and drunk most of the time, having lunch at Langan's every day. Peter Langan was drinking too and so I spent much time with him. He was my great pal, my drinking companion.

I went to Wales to be with my little mother as she was dying and drifting into senility and I visited the place where I was born. I cranked out two novels in a fortnight, having missed the deadline. I'd shamed my family. I still went to Chapel, where my grandfather had been senior deacon. I was in No Man's Land. The good part of me went to the Chapel now and I went straight from there to the pub. In that little Welsh place the people in the pub derided me for going to the Chapel, and the people in the Chapel derided me for going to the pub. So now I was nowhere. I had nobody. My soul had withered.

When my mother died I left Wales. By this time I had run out of all my careers, but I was still able to make people laugh in the pub. I was invited to read poetry at the Young Vic, and this led to a show at Ronnie Scott's club – a one-woman show; anecdotes and poems. That was my final career and that was what brought me to my rock bottom.

I was immensely successful with huge audiences. People will pay to see anybody in extremis. I was going in and out of blackouts on stage and then I got banned. I played the Edinburgh Festival two years running and the second time I had the biggest poster, the biggest room and the biggest audience and I made a load of money, but I had been banned from Pebble Mill for being drunk. Word had gone around. I had used up that career.

I couldn't do journalism. I couldn't hold a sentence in my head. I couldn't do television because I didn't know if when the time came to do it I could be sober. I could only do the night that I knew I was going to be on stage. Now my drinking took a violent downward twist. I thought 'This is brilliant. All I have to do is remain sober for an hour and a half in the 24 hours. The rest of the time I can be paralytic.'

When I came off stage at 1-30 am I was always able to find a gay club somewhere. I would be there until the morning, then go to pubs as they opened for the morning, planning to go home at lunchtime to go to bed. But I just couldn't leave the alcohol and it was getting closer and closer to when I would be on stage again at midnight. So I would have been drinking all night and all day.

One night I managed to get to bed by ten o'clock for two hours sleep and then I did that show in and out of blackouts on stage. I was petrified. I also had awful alcoholic dysentery so I couldn't trust myself to eat. I was very thin, very ill, like a butterfly. I did have close friends who stayed around – to their horror – but they were drinking too.

I went to the Dublin Festival, playing to large audiences and making a lot of money. I'd lost my voice because I was out all night, not eating and in a bad state with flu. I took a whisky one afternoon with a lot of honey and cream and I don't remember everything until the next day. I did the show but I was so drunk that I missed out the costume change and people were just snapping their seats up and demanding their money back from the box office. They didn't want to pay to see somebody drunk on stage. You can do that for free in the pubs. So I was banned.

I did one show at Ronnie Scott's (I don't know how I got through that) and then I just cancelled the rest of the tour. I gave up that career. It didn't occur to me to give up the drink instead. I blamed the *career*. I saw myself on the front page of The Stage newspaper: 'Molly Banned from Dublin for Unprofessional Conduct' which everybody in the business knows means drunk on stage. It was the first time I had been criticised for drinking and I stopped for eighteen months. That was the worst part of my 'drinking'. I was haunted by alcohol.

My two daughters whom I loved dearly had by now distanced themselves. One had chosen to live in another part of the world. The other I had humiliated and embarrassed.

There seemed nothing worth living for. Life was worse than unbearable. Waking up each morning without the drink was just the deepest agony anyone can imagine. So giving up meant nothing to me. I didn't know where to go. I just thought to give up on my own and of course inevitably I went back to drinking.

I would buy my ticket at the tube station intending to hurl myself in front of the train, but would then dribble up the stairs again, not having been able to do it. I was again in No Man's Land. Nobody knew because I told them I was writing a blockbuster.

I started to write with a friend who'd been a drinking companion and we thought we'd write TV scripts but on the second day he said what I'd been waiting for: 'Let's go for a drink.'

I had a horror for a week and that was the end of the drinking. I went to Chelsea Arts Club and had one drink and everyone said 'Moll's back, Ooh! Moll's back.' I was suddenly surrounded by pints of lager which was more than I could get down because I hated it. I had six pints and already with that first taste I was in trouble. It was only seven in the evening and already I was in a panic about what to do when this place shut at midnight. So I went, as I always did, to Ronnie's (I used to think myself a jazz afficionado. I've only been there three times since.)

I stayed at Ronnie's till three am, then back to Earl's Court. Always with people. When I had worn out one group, a fresh group would come with me to try to catch up, to join the odyssey. I would arrive before Jeffrey Bernard on the doorway of the Coach and Horses and then spend all afternoon in the Colony Room, drinking with Francis Bacon. And then back to the French House in the evening and finally I'd be back at Ronnie Scott's. Then Smithfield again. I'd smoke 100 cigarettes a night. I couldn't get drunk, but wasn't sober. I couldn't walk. I wanted to crawl to get from the building to the taxi. And drivers wouldn't take you. People said 'Molly you can't sleep here' so I was asked to leave. The ignominy of that.

And that was my last drink. And for the first time I said 'There's something wrong here.' I hadn't thought it before. And then I asked to a friend who went to a meeting of a self-help fellowship if I could take someone whose drinking was out of control to a meeting. This man said 'No.' I could only take myself. 'People have to reach rock bottom and help themselves.'

I was really disappointed, but at four in the morning I woke up and realised it *was* me who should go to the meeting. That day I was going to Camberwell to write a book with a clairvoyant. When I said I wanted to go to a meeting he replied 'You said you'd been years ago and you haven't got a drink problem.' But he hadn't seen me drinking.

He took me to Lambeth Walk and it was just the best of meetings for me because it was full of people from my background. These men were scarred – the kind you would run from if you saw one of them on a park bench. I was like that myself but couldn't see it. All I could see were these strange 'haloes' around their heads. I was hallucinating with withdrawal. They kept passing me Polo mints and they were just so *sweet* to me. I'd been used to people asking me to leave pubs and being nasty to me. They gave me a cup of tea and I was shaking it all over they saucer. I thought they'd given me too much but actually they'd only given me half a cup and still I couldn't keep it steady.

I was moved to tears by the sharing. I'd never heard about men wetting the bed nor doing the 'filing system' with bills like I did – putting them in drawers unopened. I was tremulous and emotional but I saw hope at the end of the tunnel. I saw that I wouldn't have to lead the kind of life I had been leading. I saw that after all, this fellowship was the answer. This is what had been wrong with me all along. I was an alcoholic. I accepted it from my first meeting.

When I came out I dumped four packets of cigarettes in the dustbin because I knew that if one addiction was going to be knocked on the head the other two would follow because I'd go into a bar, take that first drink and would feel the click, the personality change, and then I'd reach for a cigarette and look around for which bloke to pull.

I never had another cigarette or drink or that promiscuity ever since. I became celibate for four and a half years and then I joyfully relinquished that this summer.

At first in recovery I was physically ill. I didn't have a very understanding doctor. My doctor who likes a bit of a drink himself always said: 'Oh, I'd rather have you drunk than fat . . . ' because I started to eat and went overboard on sugar, but now eating is starting to settle down.

My concentration improved. My financial situation took longer. My friend D took me to my second meeting in Sloane Square. I told him I'd been to a meeting and he said he'd been waiting ten years to hear me said I'd joined the fellowship. I wondered why he hadn't said something and he said 'You'd have told me to clear off if I'd told you you had a drink problem' and of course I would. I would have been outraged at such a suggestion.

I had a spiritual experience in that first meeting and with the love in the room I knew I was going to be all right. I found there that my life was fit to have.

Now I was on a spiritual journey. I went to sit in churches which I hadn't done before. I went to India and there found a peace which caused a shift in my life which showed me that the hovel I'd chosen to live in in Bethnal Green was wrong, that it had been an unhealthy choice, close to strip clubs and violence, shouting, swearing, drunkenness at all hours, broken windows right under my nose.

It was like my fix, behind my shutters feeling my heart racing. The violence that I was used to. I felt at home. But not after India, not after that sweetness and peace. Within a week of coming back I said to myself 'This isn't right. This isn't recovery.' So I got on my knees and prayed and asked for a new place to live. And that week a friend rang and said there was a flat in Chelsea, a nice one I could afford as that very same week I was given the job of agony aunt. So it has gone on.

And in recovery I've had three grandchildren who are younger than my recovery. And the situation with both my daughters is absolutely idyllic.

My closest friend is ninety. She's a very fine woman, the god-mother of my children and really like a surrogate mother. She never knew about my drinking. She hasn't got any 'isms' and she's published two books since she was eighty-four so I think 'Well now Moll, you've got thirty years left' and that is longer than I was drinking.

It's brilliant.

• SARAH STACEY •

◇

Sarah Stacey is a journalist who lives in London.

I'm now 42 and a journalist. I stopped drinking just after I was 29. In my 20s I thought and hoped that I would be dead by the time I was 35, but I didn't have the courage to kill myself.

I was working as a temporary cook in a big country house in the East of England. My usual pattern was to help myself (which is a polite way to say 'steal') to drink. I was very bold about it. I was found by these terribly nice people I was cooking for, sitting by the drinks cabinet contemplating whether I should have Curaçao or Cointreau. I was plunged into shame. I went up to my bedroom and I packed my straw-basket (which I carried all my worldly possessions in). It was nearly midnight and I set off to the village pond to kill myself.

That episode is terribly poignant because it illustrates very much the kind of lost child I was – the total departure from reality. What I was doing was what I had read in Victorian novels. I wanted to be the 'disgraced girl found in village pond'.

I always had this extraordinary reaction to what was really a mild chastisement from the people I was with, and it showed that I was completely unable to ask for help. The guilt and shame that consumed me were the accumulation of feeling that I was a wrong person, that I was of no value, that I didn't *deserve* to exist with these ordinary decent people. I seemed gross.

But here I am at 42, happy, successful, reasonably well-adjusted, but most of all I love and am loved and I *trust*. I expect to be loved and I expect to get on with other people. It's a complete 180 degree turn-around from the way I had felt since I was little. I see now that my childhood and adolescence were amazingly coloured by the fact that one of my parents was a drinker.

I am quite interested in the genetic side of it and I've done a lot of work on it. I do accept the fact that in many cases it is a genetic predisposition coupled with a lot of environmental triggers. In my case, you can see the genetic disposition because it went through succeeding generations. My grandfather who was labelled a genius was also an alcoholic, only in those days it was called a 'dipsomaniac'. My father was called a manic depressive. I don't know whether that is actually true. My younger brother can be a very heavy drinker but is not an alcoholic.

I accept the definition of alcoholic as somebody who is alcohol-dependent, someone who, after the first drink or first drug, can't trust themselves. I have *no way* of controlling myself after that first drink.

My clearest memory of drink and myself is that at about the age of eight I was given red wine. My father was a Francophile and I can remember him saying to me 'I'm going to teach you how to drink now, because if any young blood tries to get you drunk you'll be able to cope with it.' Well that's exactly the opposite to what happened. I grew up with the notion that drinking was good. I also grew up with the notion that drinking was a compensation and a consolation.

When I was about sixteen I was running the house as my mother was ill. I saw myself as Katy in 'What Katy Did', gathering the reins of the household in my small but capable hands. I saw the bottles on the side table one day and thought, well after I've given Mummy her lunch, and after I've taken the dogs for a walk and after I've done the washing up, I'm going to give myself a drink because this is what people do to make themselves feel better. So my thinking about drink was very clear. It's a good thing, it's a grown-up thing and it's a reward. I had absolutely no concept at that time of addiction. However, I do realize looking back on it that my mind's eye view of myself was of a lost child.

Only after thirteen years of sobriety am I beginning to understand and adopt the child inside the grown-up me. I never felt at peace with myself. I never felt self-confident. I never felt that I could trust in my own adequacy to meet other people's requirements, demands, or expectations. I never knew what they wanted and I certainly never felt I had a right to decide what I wanted.

My opinion of my own wants and needs was entirely coloured by other people's wants and needs. I was losing myself entirely as a person. Equally all during that time the effect of the addictions was growing. I would come in late from heavy evenings drinking in Soho or wherever and I would be *beyond* drunk.

When I was first in the programme a lot of people said to me, 'You know the great thing about being in recovery is that we discover who we are', meaning there is a core to everybody's personality which has been hidden by drink and drugs and the effects of the continual lack of self esteem. They are trusting that there really *is* somebody in there. My great fear about this was that I would find that unlike everybody else around me, there's wasn't anybody there. I remember that the image of this came to me very strongly when I was walking down the Flower Walk in Kensington Gardens thinking about discovering who I was and I thought 'I wonder who is there?'

My feeling about myself was that I was like a soft-centered sweet, with a brittle outside. You might get through the brittle outside but all you would find inside was an amorphous sticky mass. Instead of having a core being which was Sarah, a valid person with opinions and moods and wants and worth, there was just this sticky mass. I remember thinking there must be a Sarah in there somewhere and it was as if I was putting out my hand walking down the Flower Walk in the sun and saying 'Is Sarah there where my finger tips are, or is she *there* . . . or . . . where . . . ?'

I had a lot of blackouts. I used to wet my bed and collapse in blackouts in the gutter. I used to stagger into pubs well after closing time and demand drinks. Usually I was picked up by a man, quite often a taxi driver. I would be taken home, sleep with them, and wake up seeing a strange person in my bed whom I didn't know. It was a feeling of being consumed by grief and shame and fear and revulsion at yourself and at the other person.

The other person had colluded in this and the only thing to do was to get them out as quickly as possible. Some of them actually were terribly kind and sometimes I think actually they just wanted to look after me. They were often very kind, as you might be to a child.

I remember somebody who found me collapsed in the gutter in Portobello and took me home. The next morning I couldn't understand why I was dressed in one of their caftans. They told me that I had fallen into a puddle but what had really happened was that I had wet myself. I was terribly touched because they were behaving so decently and kindly, yet I in contrast was a lush, a hopeless case. I did everything everybody else did in active alcoholism. I stole, I lost jobs; I lost my conscience.

I talked to my great friend about this sense of feeling so awful. (She's not an alcoholic, she's a social worker.) She said 'Why didn't you tell *me*?' I said 'I couldn't. I was in the gutter and you were so wonderful.' She said 'Well, I thought you were wonderful.' I have never been more surprised. What I understand her to have meant was that there were wonderful qualities that weren't erased entirely by the drink, although they were hidden to me.

To earn money I worked as a secretary. I also sewed and cooked.

One of the reasons I cooked so much was because there was access all the time to the drinks cupboard. I would haul myself out of bed, out of blackouts. Often there wasn't a drink in the house so I used to go to work simply because I needed a bloody Mary.

I was very fearful of everything. That is another point about being an active addict, but it may not be true of everyone. I was never an addict who stood up and danced on the table, although I did try it and found the results were much worse than if I hid in the broom cupboard. I had no way of communicating with other people. You are either pretending to be better than you are or hiding how awful you are. You can never say 'I am *Me*. I have a right, I may not be as pretty as you are, I may not have as nice a house, I may not be the same in any way but I am all right. And I trust that you will take me on that valuation.' I can actually do that now. I really can. I feel alright about myself.

That has come at first through blind faith, and after that it was knowing that I was loved and supported by people who had known exactly what I was like at my worst. There was no deception ever involved. Now that I have sobriety it's not just other people in the programme who I can tell exactly what I was like, I am quite able to tell *anybody*. As a journalist I have written and talked about my own alcoholism. I think really that the biggest testimonial to the fellowship of the self-help programme is that I trust that only good will come of me being honest. I trust that if I don't let my ego get in the way, the right thing will happen.

What happened was that I was a drunk, who tried to throw away life and not only was I given a second crack at that, but I was given a sense of life and purpose that literally was unthought of when I was drinking. It's a sense of humanity. It's sense of being linked with other people in a way that is completely impossible when you're enduring and being immersed in the solitude of active addiction.

I came into the programme three and a half years later. I knew I was an alcoholic at the age of 26, three and a half years before giving up. One morning I had got up at 6 am and cleared up after a party. I started drinking. At 9.30 am I phoned work and I would be late. By 11 am I was seriously depressed. I phoned work again and made more excuses, phoned work a third time and said I was going to kill myself, and they sent somebody over to try and stop me.

It was my great girlfriend, the one who is now a social worker, and I told her with great difficulty that I thought I was an alcoholic. It was the first time I admitted it.

She said 'You're not an alcoholic, you're a nice girl. What you need is a change of job and a change of environment and you need a home' and she very sweetly offered me a home which in fact has been mine whenever I chose to have, until this day.

What she didn't know about was addiction, and that changing my environment or changing job would never change my addiction. I went up to Scotland and had a lovely time. I got blind drunk about twice and then left what was actually a safe environment. I came back to London and went out with a couple of friends. I was picked up in the gutter, drunk, that night. It took me three more years of knowing I was an alcoholic to come into the Fellowship. During those years, every time I went into an off licence I knew exactly what was happening to me, but I had no idea what to do about it. I decided that I was going to die. I decided that I would just drink, drink, drink and that with any luck I would die by the age of 35. I was only 28.

I was so helpless, it was not a bit romantic. I did not have a good time. I did not have wonderful romances. I did not go anywhere. I hardly did anything. I was in a fifth floor flat with a phone which was locked. There was no bathroom, the lavatory stank, I smelled, I somehow got to work most days. As I said, I was cooking, and I got to work in order to be able to drink. I wanted a friend who was a psychiatrist to say 'The only way to deal with you is to put you in a locked ward because there is no hope for you.' All I wanted was to be kept doped, and out of harm's way. I had literally no hope at all. I did keep on putting one foot in front another because I was too frightened, too unknowing to do anything else.

One night I saw a woman on a television programme. She was in the outpatients department of a hospital doing basketwork, and she said that she had been a drinking alcoholic and that she had got better. I was electrified. I could see from her eyes that she was free. She had terrible bags under her eyes but they were actually alive and sparkling. She had this power. It was the first time I had heard anyone say they had this drinking problem and they had got better. It went rolling through into my subconscious. And funnily enough, a month after I'd got into the programme, which was about two months after I had seen that television programme, somebody said to me that my eyes looked alive for the first time.

However I didn't get into the programme then. I went and house-kept for a drunken old MP. I went on a major bender one weekend and I woke up on the fifth day in a sun-filled attic room with a half-empty bottle of Scotch in the crook of my arm. And that was the last drink that I'd ever thought about taking. I got up and replaced the drink that I'd stolen from the house. For the first time in ages I didn't put a stiff measure of whisky into my coffee. I actually knew what I was going to do.

I looked up a self-help group meeting in the telephone directory and I found it. It was a very strange feeling because I could swear I had looked for it before and not found it. I got straight through to Marie who was answering the phone. She said 'Do you think you have a drinking problem?' I said 'Yes,' and she asked 'Would you like to go to a meeting?' I said 'Yes'. She told me afterwards that I was the first person who had ever laughed. She said 'Why did you laugh?' It was because it was such a colossal sense of relief, that somebody had asked me direct questions to which I could answer 'Yes.' She did ask me if I'd like somebody to come and collect me but I couldn't quite deal with that.

That was the first time I went to work with such hope. It was like black to white. It was the most extraordinary thing. And it was the first time I suppose that I was experiencing this communication with other people.

I went to my first meeting in Chelsea at 7.30 pm. I had walked over from Westminster, I didn't dare go in early. At 7.29 I fell in through the doors like a startled rabbit, into the arms of a grey-haired woman named Ann who was beautifully dressed, like someone out of Country Life magazine. She said to me 'You must be Sarah. Have you had a drink today?' I said 'No' and she was terribly pleased. She introduced me to other people and said 'Isn't it wonderful? She hasn't had a drink today' and I thought 'This is all I have to do. And everybody is happy for me, with me.'

I was asked if I would like to say anything at the meeting and I said 'Well, I don't know how to encapsulate ten years' drinking' and they shut me up terribly quickly which was probably a good thing. So I sat there and listened. The only thing I really remember is a man called David saying 'If you've got a drinking problem, you're in the right place.'

I was feeling very shaky. When everybody got up afterwards to clear the chairs away, I was still sitting there because, I wasn't sure that I could stand up. I wasn't even certain if I could hold my plastic cup which was full of hot tea. I remember somebody coming up to me and very sweetly holding my hand and saying 'Perhaps you'd like to get up now and we can put the chair away.' I felt an extraordinary sense of warmth and affection and felt that there was no more being demanded of me.

I learnt to live in the day, sometimes in the hour or the minute. I didn't have to be frightened about what had happened or what was going to happen. I wasn't consumed by fear and I could actually trust the people around me. It was absolutely mind-blowing. It was a sensation I hadn't felt for decades, not since my nanny looked after me as a child. For the first time I was adequate. And also there, in that moment I was surrounded by people who cared.

I remember going through that first sober summer. I came into the programme on 18th April 1978 and I remember the summer being a most extraordinary gift. I was so happy, almost as if the summer was tangible. It was quivering and brilliant and scintillating and full of wonderful colours and yellow sunshine. It was having a place to go and having people to ring.

I have to say though that in the first month I didn't dare pick up the phone. I only dared when I thought I was going to drink again. It was a sense not only of direction but of security and for the first time it was a sense of life. It was a sense of not wanting to die. In fact it was the absolute opposite – it was wanting to live. I used to sit in cars paralysed with fear that I might end up in a car crash, that I might lose this extraordinary thing I had found. I used to think 'I can't bear to die now. I've suddenly found life.' I had things to do. I had films to go to. I had people to have meals with. Of course it wasn't all rosy, but it was wonderful.

On the first anniversary of my joining the Twelve Step programme of recovery, I was at Victoria and they said as a treat I could take the meeting. I thought that was the most frightening treat anyone had ever given me and I shook. But it *was* actually a treat and I remember they brought me out a birthday cake at the end and everyone clapped. The next morning I was so over-excited about being one year sober I woke up at six o'clock in the morning, and I thought, 'I am a year sober,' I felt that my body was screaming with joy.

I have never rebelled against the fellowship because I felt that I'd made all my slips before I came in. Occasionally I saw mirages of brandy bottles and I have wanted to drink at stages throughout sobriety. I think as an alcoholic it is a perfectly normal thing to want to do. I had to develop a mechanism which allowed me to acknowledge that feeling of wanting to drink and yet say absolutely in parallel 'Now, you don't have to do it. And you know what will happen if you do.'

I used to sit in front of bottles which seemed to gravitate towards me at dinner parties before I was actually able to say outright to somebody 'Could you just move it? It means all the worst things in the world to me.' I would say to myself, like a mantra, 'I'm Sarah, I'm an alcoholic and I am powerless over alcohol.' It works every time.

I never had to take the drink and I do actually believe that you can't be saying to yourself 'I'm Sarah, I'm an alcoholic, I'm powerless over alcohol' *and* drink. You don't have room in your conscious mind and in your subconscious for the two things.

I had to go through this saga of when I said 'I want a drink', it didn't have to be alcoholic. It could be anything that satisfied the part of my mind that was crying out for a crutch saying 'I want a drink, I want a drink, I want a drink' by saying instead' I can have a drink and I can also talk to somebody about the problem which is making me want to lose myself.'

I was able to be upfront about being an 'alkie' because my friends were all so proud of me. At one quite grand dinner party with three MPs and some journalists, a doctor was talking pure rubbish about addiction. I went to the loo to calm myself, and when I came back, said 'I have to declare an interest. I've been in AA for nine years.' I told them what had happened to me.

It was as if the table was electrified. I didn't know what the reaction was going to be. In fact the MPs and journalists there all came up and hugged me. And so I think one has to trust one's self. It is fine to say these things and yet you also can trust yourself that you won't overdo it and that you'll say it in the right way. If you do it with the right motivation, you won't be on an ego trip. People can see you have a solution to an appalling problem. I think there is such misunderstanding about the illness and ignorance about the solution that it makes people think there *isn't* a solution, and everybody thinks it's your fault. A lot of us feel so terribly ashamed of ourselves.

For me it's been very important to say who I am, but without being a drama queen. And I certainly was a terrible drama queen when I came into the programme. I hadn't realised how far I'd gone in the direction of feeling inferior and how much I'd tried to compensate by trying to be superior. The way I tried to be superior was not only to try and puff up what I did but was to put down other people. And that was one of the things that made me feel so terribly uncomfortable.

I was forever gnawing away at things that were nothing to do with me. I could never make myself leave well alone. It is important to me now to have parameters that say 'These things are my problem. They are things I can do something about. And these things are your province. They are either your problem or they're something which affects you and not me. Something which you have the knowledge to do something about and I don't.'

I didn't start writing until I was nine years sober. I went on feeling

I was stupid for ten years in sobriety. I used to compensate by being completely obsessed with work. One of my sponsees was going completely batty. She told me 'You are upsetting me dreadfully because you are so obsessed with work you are not concentrating on what I'm saying.' My preoccupation with work was just outright fear that I wouldn't get what I was doing right. After she tackled me I did get a kind of balance.

I saw a movie about passion called 'Jesus of Montreal' which actually seemed to act as a catalyst in the sense that it brings a notion of you to the surface that you might not acknowledge otherwise. I thought if I put the same kind of energy into my work, into researching it, sorting out how it should go, and actually *writing* it as I do into worrying about it, then I would do a lot better and feel a lot better. What I do is sit there projecting, so obsessed with worry about the results, that I can't concentrate on actually doing the work

Although journalism is very lonely, at the end of the day if you haven't done it perfectly, you will have editors helping you and subs correcting what you've done. It is a team effort, but I have never been able to see or approach any aspect of life as a team. I've always been out there by myself, terrified, and setting about the reversal of that belief system has been one of the most important and difficult things that has happened to me.

To acknowledge the fact that I can offer help to other people and they can offer help to me is vital. You need me today, tomorrow I will need you desperately. We are both giving freely what we have been given. That's it.

I don't know what God is. I'm not a Christian. I'm not religious. I have an extremely strong faith and I like different aspects of different religions. I was terribly happy recently in India with a group of people who see faith, meditation and worship of a source of power not only as a part of every day life but *as part of every minute of everyday life*.

What saved me on the programme was the third step – being told I was in the care of God. I realised that all my life I had wanted to feel cared for and it didn't matter who or what God is. My first sponsor who was a Buddhist said to me 'You have to be God to know the nature of God'.

I do trust the higher power and believe it will never fail you. As to the steps, if you do something for long enough it does become part of you. Occasionally I do have to think of them word for word but I think you do start living in a way which reflects what you believe in.

The programme is a set of guidelines, the script that I never had.

It's as simple as that. I had to confront my past, look at it, acknowledge it, put it away and begin to live in the minute.

I used to think 'I will be happy when . . . ' or 'If only such and such happened I'd be all right.' Now I believe 'The only reality you have is this minute. The only question is am I all right *now*?'

· Tom ·

Tom is a dancer and actor and lives in London.

The first drink I liked was lager. I remember drinking it when Dad was planting vegetables in the garden; he had left half a can of Harp. Before that I hadn't liked the taste.

The first time I remember feeling the effects of wine was when I was ten and went to see the film 2001. Afterwards we went to an Italian restaurant for a meal. We had some wine and I remember likening it to the psychedelic colours in the movie. I went to the loo and thought 'I don't like this feeling. I wouldn't want it to be any more than this.'

Some time elapsed before I started drinking pints. That happened when I was about fourteen and going out with a girl. We used to go to a pub on Sunday evenings where we would sit round a table with her parents and that was when I first used to get a bit drunk. We all got a little under the weather but it was fun, it was jolly.

I remember going to London to see a dance company with a group from school. I sneaked off at lunchtime and went to the pub for a lager. It really had an effect. I went back to the group in the afternoon and had a giggle because I had got away with it, and not been found out.

I first went to a gay pub when I was fifteen and I needed to be fortified with Dutch courage. I had a Bloody Mary. I was very nervous and having that drink made me feel grown up. A chap I met there was joking and said 'You look very nervous'. I concocted a story about having just seen a car crash down the road, which explained why I was shaking. I was conscious of drink being useful at that time. A quick drink and it calmed my nerves.

My experience at sixteen was of being heterosexual, being in school and having a girlfriend. I really started drinking when I went away to school. It seemed everyone else was into it. Dad was drinking heavily at that time and there was a lot of stuff at home for parties. I used to drink to excess a lot of the time. I remember getting reeling drunk on gin and not being able to stand up, and thinking it was the most appalling thing. I had a long discussion with the history teacher (this was a co-ed progressive boarding school and we weren't allowed to drink). I had been out to buy a quart of cider which I had brought back to school. I argued at length with him. I gave him reasons why I should get my cider back. I knew what alcoholism was all about because my father was an alcoholic and had just started in a fellowship of recovering alcoholics. I got my cider back.

At the age of seventeen I had left school and I started at sixth form college. I went to London at weekends. One of the girls at college whom I really liked was an alcoholic. I loved the sensation of getting together with friends and having a really good heart-to-heart and uproarious laughs. These were still the good times.

My drinking progressed quickly from fifteen to twenty. While other friends took time to drink, I was very fast. When I started going to London, alcohol played a big part in my life but my approach to it was quite schoolboyish. I then visited Paris where I drank wine and smoked dope. I had been smoking dope since I was fifteen. In Paris I was fascinated by the way the workmen used to start drinking aper-itifs early in the morning to warm themselves. Rather a romantic sort of feeling.

I came back to London and, because I had started to go to clubs, there was conflict at home. I was no longer fitting in. There was a sort of alienation which I suppose started because my life was at variance with the way the family had perceived life should be.

I remember having a hefty joint and it calmed my nerves and there was a sense of contentment inside me. I was conscious that drink and drugs could provide a short cut to a sense of calm and well-being. It was a druggy year. I got into pills and valium because Dad had them around the house. I got into the effect of downers, tranquillisers and alcohol – a lethal concoction, but I liked it because it produced a feeling of serenity. It was around 17/18 that the alcohol really started to conflict with a normal way of living.

It started to cause serious problems at home. I had a recently sober father who was newly into the programme and he was aware now that his son was having problems too. He was angry about that and frustrated and worried. The family were going to live abroad and I was given an ultimatum: clean up my act or stay behind. So I said I would clean up my act but I didn't, and so when we got to South America there was trouble. Problems increased because there was much more trouble around and there were temptations and unscru-pulous people round every corner.

I was still under the influence of my family. I was living with them so there was a lot I didn't get up to. I wasn't very promiscuous abroad. It wasn't suitable. But I liked going to clubs and there I had my really reckless times on alcohol.

I'd had times in France when I'd been legless on rough red wine but in South America I had a night when I hit the whisky, beer and wine, and was unaware that getting into a car and driving was a wrong thing to do. But I wanted to get to a club and I was determined to find it, haring around the highways, up and down different roads. I didn't find the place and eventually got arrested for drunk and reckless driving. I had a shock and stopped drinking for a few weeks and went to self-help twelve-step meetings but didn't keep it up. All the time I thought I had an adult view of what it was like to be worldly and a drug-dependent person.

There was a 24-hour jail sentence attached to the drink-drive offences which was very unpleasant. Things were very messy then. I was taking valium and my own sexual ambivalence coupled with the drink and drugs made me a very difficult person to be around. As I recall it, I was an embarrassment to my family and I was conscious of this.

It was suggested I went to Paris. Very quickly. The suggestion was made and 48 hours later I was there. The first month was spent going from place to place; eventually I found a job in a restaurant and was helped by the boss to find an apartment. She gave me an advance to find a little place and I had a job.

After the first fairly crazy month I veered between going out and being on top form and making sure that I looked immaculate and was being popular, to other nights when I looked like a drunken harridan. I would put make-up on dreadfully and look like a nightmare because I was so drunk and my judgement went.

Sometimes I could handle things; sometimes I was out of control. I got into more and more scrapes, and then I really got sick and didn't know what it was. I thought I was dying but the illness was cured by very good treatment in hospital.

I was having injections and was told that I wasn't to drink. But I did. I got into a routine of brown beer and haziness; the nice feeling that life was OK now after one drink. But I couldn't hold it there. And of course because I was so young I got into bad situations with people who would take advantage of me. I got out of some very tight corners by legging it.

There was an unscrupulous lawyer who used to have open house for lots of young people who liked a good time and liked to hang out. I was also going out with a 30-year-old Parisian woman who was very helpful in getting me out of trouble. She suggested I might leave Paris and go back home. She could see I was in a mess.

One weekend when I was at the lawyer's house he had some Corsican mafia drug dealers round – colleagues who used to throw parties. Teenagers used to go along. I was among them. But we were just pawns. We could have been bumped off very quickly if we overstepped the mark.

I was just a druggy English boy who was sometimes good for a laugh. I couldn't *see* the risks but I did have a sense of them – a sense that I needed to get away. The job at the restaurant was winding down because I wasn't reliable. I used to turn up late and pinch from the till. I wasn't the only one. It was very much like a recaltriant family at this place, with hippies and people like me. The owner put up with a lot.

Eventually I lost my place there. I got back to England in October and had a reunion with the family, now back from South America. Initially this was fine. I got a place to live and then began drinking heavily, London-style, in pubs. I realised I could go to the doctors and get my own prescription for tranquillisers saying I 'needed them for my nerves'. I never really needed them for my nerves. I got into more and more things that were difficult to control. I was very unreliable.

The culmination was a family party which involved a lot of humiliation for me. I made a complete fool of myself. I was switching in and out of personalities, all brought on by a combination of drink and drugs.

It was suggested I go to my father's self-help meeting. I went to work one day and found I had lost my job. I went home bereft. That afternoon it came to me that I should go to a meeting and I made an effort to go. I phoned various sources that afternoon, including Samaritans. I went to a gay AA meeting at the Crypt and got into the fellowship. That was at the end of 1978 and until April 1979 I was going to meetings regularly. I met my first friends in the Fellowship – B who was a 50s showgirl and J who was an academic. He was 32 and became my sponsor.

But then I made a wrong move. The Fellowship says 'keep things simple' and don't put yourself in the line of fire if you don't want to take a risk. I moved into a place with a fellow who liked having young people around. He was a boozer, but he could cope and I couldn't. I had a drink and then went and got a prescription. A lapse. Two lapses in one month. March to April. The second one was severe.

I was crying. My face puffed up. I had damaged my liver. This proved to me I seriously needed help. So B, who had been through addiction treatment, got me an interview with a friend of hers. The physical effects calmed down. I went to see B's friend and after initial screening I was told I could attend the clinic full-time as a resident.

I got into a course of treatment in June 1979. I was twenty years old. I had two weeks of detox though I didn't really need it as I had done that for myself. I was young and I hadn't been an around-the-clock drinker but more a reckless, out-of-control drinker. I did two weeks without drink, and then subsequent twelve weeks, and *it changed my life*.

It involved AA meetings on a regular basis; every evening we would go off in a coach. It was very communal and behavioural. We learned to behave and how to deal with criticism and how to deal with situations and events. We had occupational therapy and talks and counselling. We counselled each other and had counselling from doctors. We had to write a life story. In the first six weeks we discussed our lives up to that date. Then we wrote it down and read it out and had it analysed by an Angelo and Diabolo system. This worked by one person speaking as an Angel putting your good side to the group, followed by the Devil putting the other side, showing up all your bad qualities and where you were lacking. In the next six weeks we learned from it and built on our life story.

When I came out I was in some indecision as to where to live. At first, after coming out of treatment in September 1979 I was going to a half-way house. That didn't happen and in the end I was glad.

I was able to move back into the countryside, first to my parents' house and then into my own little place nearby in November 1979. It gave me my own home with some autonomy away from the group and too much institutionalisation. It also gave me a chance to get back with my family which did happen over the following two years.

I went to local self-help meetings regularly. The power of the fellowship was very strong in me and I got a manual job. I had heard at a meeting in Surrey – from a woman who had subsequently become successful in business – how, in recovery, she had first got a job at Sainsbury's doing manual work and how useful it had been to her recovery. I identified with that and felt I could justify doing one. But I did feel I should be doing something more than pushing a broom and packing boxes. That, however, is what I did for just under two years.

I joined the local amateur dramatic society and someone there suggested I should pursue the theatre as a career. P, someone else I knew from group, suggested I further my education. I made a friend in the group, M, who has stayed my friend. Having these friendships, having these links, being able to sustain relationships in sobriety, has been important. I did act on good suggestions in those days.

I was somewhat successful in the amateur dramatic group. I enjoyed the feedback and decided I would try to go to a drama school. I made some applications. I opted for one of the two courses I was offered. One in which I could get a degree in dance and drama training, and that got me back into dancing which is something for which I had always had a flair. I had really wanted to do it when I was about 15 but that had got sidetracked by my wayward way of life.

And so I did my course and that was a good time, all in sobriety. I got a degree and that is how I've lived my life ever since then, without a drink or pills.

I haven't maintained AA meetings. I still get 'dry drunk' anxiety attacks which trigger old reactions at times when everything seems to much. I still rely on the slogans and the very deep seated messages of twelve step fellowship, keeping it simple and just relaxing, unwinding from tension and self-doubt and self-centredness. All these things can lead you up the garden path into needing an escape. I am conscious of the dangers that face any drug-dependent person.

Performing and being liked have always been important to me. I identify with other performers because it is a peculiar way of life; a self-centred one and not a lot of people could cope with it, but it is rewarding.

After graduating I did an arduous course of one year with a good dance company where I had first gone as a teenager. There they taught me what it was like to be a dancer, the hardness of it. So I have chosen to make that my career so far. I love working. I still have problems with over-sensitivity, reacting too quickly and getting tense, but I've learned not to end up in difficult situations, to keep my trap shut and let the moment pass.

Without sobriety there would be no basis on which to build anything. At the moment I'm doing one of the hardest jobs I have ever done and I like the challenge.

· BRIAN WELLS ·

*Brian Wells is a consultant psychiatrist, living in London.
He is one of the founders of SHARP.*

I am 42, a consultant psychiatrist working in the National Health Service and one of the founders of SHARP. I'm 11 years in recovery.

My father was in the airforce and life was really a series of different airforce stations all around the world. When I was nine my father was posted to France where I got involved in playing baseball and became influenced by all things American. I went to an international school which had children from NATO forces. Looking back, one of my first mind-altering experiences was sitting in an American base eating a banana split having just hit a home run in a little league baseball game. A record came on the juke box. It was called 'Diana' by Paul Anka and I vividly remember the feeling in my stomach when this music started. I stopped what I was doing and I was just moved into a different place listening to it. I went to the juke box and played it about four times. I was knocked sideways. It was a similar feeling to the other times that I experienced other mind-altering sources of stimulation (such as drugs and alcohol).

I came back to boarding-school in Suffolk. At the age of 12, a friend and I decided to get drunk, to see what it was like. We saved up our pocket money and went out of bounds by the river with a bottle of Emva Cream sherry and a flagon of cider. I had a few swigs and passed him the bottle. While he was drinking, it began to have an effect on me. I just loved the feeling, whereas my friend started looking pale and threw up into the river. I remember thinking 'Good – that means there'll be more for me' and we staggered back into school having consumed most of the sherry. I was staggering because I was actually drunk. I was singing and shouting and drawing attention to myself.

I never drank alcohol without wanting to feel that effect that I felt the first time I drank. I never drank because I liked the bouquet of a fine wine or the taste of real ale. I didn't actually *like* the taste of alcoholic drinks very much at all, but I loved the effect that I got.

During my school days, whenever I had the opportunity to drink, I always drank as much as I could in order to get that feeling. My friends all did the same and it was all pretty normal schoolboy stuff.

I did well at school and got a place at Cambridge to study medicine. I took a year off between leaving school and going up to University so I went to the United States where my parents had been posted. I worked at various jobs and I would occasionally drink with other lads. On a Saturday night we'd have a jug of beer in a pizza house and again, I'd always like to drink and feel that effect. I was fairly responsible and when I was driving I would not get pissed.

Later that year I found myself in San Francisco. This was 1967 and I'd heard all about people in San Francisco doing interesting things. I saw all these people with tambourines and long hair wandering about the Haight Ashbury district and I thought it terribly phony, I didn't feel drawn into it at all. They were handing joints around and saying 'Here, try some of this. This'll turn you on man.' They were mainly high-school kids who'd come in for the weekend wearing blankets, shaking tambourines, drifting and talking garbage. Being a well brought up, middle-class lad I wasn't about to try smoking these 'reefers' so I didn't get involved in that movement at all.

After a couple of months, I moved down the coast to San Diego. I was with a bunch of people I really did like who were surfing, driving Corvettes Stingrays, going out with girls, and stealing food from supermarkets. I really did want to be part of this crowd. They also were smoking grass, which they had brought across the border from Tijuana. I tried it and nothing happened. However, the second time I tried it, I got stoned. I remember vividly where I was sitting, what record I was listening to, how that strawberry milkshake tasted. It was just a wonderful experience. I had a great time living there, smoking dope, but not drinking much because it wasn't cool to drink, and we didn't have a lot of money.

When the year was over, I back to university and almost immediately got involved with a group of people who had long hair, who were listening to Pink Floyd through headphones, going to Andy Warhol movies, and smoking hash. You had to roll it up in cigarettes, and for that reason I started smoking nicotine. It was peer group attraction. I wanted to be part of this group that was superior to everyone else, had slightly greater vision, and was more grown up than everyone else who was cycling around Cambridge.

These people smoked cannabis in a fairly sensible way. I always got really stoned. *I was always the person who held on to the joint*. I would wake up, have a joint, wander round Cambridge, have some breakfast, then listen to some music, and wouldn't do any work at all. At this point I'd got away from my family, away from the control of my 'military' father. I didn't have to go to any lectures, I didn't *have* to do anything, didn't have to take any exams. Basically I had a three year holiday.

I don't have many regrets, but I do regret having wasted so much time at university. I could have done something useful. I just wasted time, ran a mobile discotheque and discovered girls. I spent as much time as I could in London which seemed to be a much more happening place than little insular Cambridge where I knew everybody and was bored silly.

During my third year I did have to take exams. I hadn't done any work so somebody said 'Why don't you try taking some of these tablets? Stay up and work through the night and you'll feel great.' I did so and I began to lose my fear of taking drugs. I tried taking amphetamines and I just loved the feeling they gave me. I worked for several weeks, staying up all night and studying anatomy and all the things I should have done over the previous three years. I got a rather bad degree but it was good enough to get a place at medical school.

So I came to London, still smoking quite a lot of dope, and rapidly got involved with a group of nurses. At that time they could get hold of Mandrax, Valium, Mogadon, whatever, off the tray at work. (They didn't have the sort of rigid checks they have now.) Soon life became a series of cocktails. I would wake up, take a stimulant, take some Valium to keep me calm. In the evening, I would take some Tuinal or Mandrax, maybe have a drink or two, and smoke some cannabis.

For the first time I started to get problems as a result of taking drugs. I would fall asleep at the wrong time. I would ride up and down the Northern Line having tried to get off at Golders Green. I got evicted from flats and people began to get fed up with me. At dinner parties I would fall over. Landladies became alarmed because I'd be falling about at eleven o'clock after a few Mandrax and several pints of beer. I was more interested in hanging around recording studios and being seen as someone who always had an ounce of dope than I was in going to medical school.

I spent three years doing this. I actually made a record in 1973 that reached number one in Hong Kong. I saw myself as a long-haired, slightly misunderstood person who had all these different scenes going on.

During this time I used to go to John and Yoko's house in Ascot. They had just recorded 'Imagine' there and then went off to New

York and never came back. A friend of mine had married their secretary and they lived in a coach house at the back of the big house. I liked being part of all that. It seemed to be exciting and there seemed to be powerful things going on. I was seduced by all this.

The medical school wasn't at all impressed when I failed my exams. They warned me that if I failed again I would have to leave. I was now married to another medical student and started to work very hard for six months. I would get up at six, go to the hospital do the the pharmacology and obstetrics that I had neglected to do and work for twelve hours. I stopped smoking cannabis, but I still took Valium. By this time I was taking between 20 and 50 mgs every day and that was part of my normal life. If I stopped taking it I felt terrible.

On my way home from the hospital, I used to call in at the pub. First I had a gin and bitter lemon. On day number three I had a double, and within a few weeks I was walking into that pub at six o'clock and ordering a triple gin and bitter lemon. *I don't know anyone who has ordered a triple anything who hasn't got some sort of alcohol problem*. Normal drinkers don't do that. I would get mildly pissed, then hang out for the rest of the evening and listen to music, and wake up the next morning and work.

That went on for about six months and I couldn't see it was anything abnormal. My wife and I both qualified as doctors in July 1974 and started working very hard in different hospitals. During that time I hardly smoked any cannabis. When we were off duty we'd meet up in a restaurant, share a bottle of wine and fall asleep exhausted. I actually discovered that I really enjoyed doctoring, but during that first job I had a kidney stone. I was taken to casualty where they gave me an injection of pethidine. The feeling from this stuff started to work on me in a just wonderful way. *It was like something I had been looking for my whole life*. I immediately started to *pretend* I was in pain just to get more pethidine. I was admitted to hospital for an operation and stayed there for a week. During that period of time I was ringing the bell even though I wasn't in much pain, because I wanted to experience the feeling that this stuff gave me. I convalesced and then went back to work. There were no other problems with drugs or alcohol for a year.

I then started in general practice and my wife went to Northampton. We were having a difficult time together and within a short period I developed a very serious drug problem. I was helping myself to opiate drugs from my black bag. For the next two years life became a series of crises.

I knew that what I was doing was crazy. I couldn't see that smoking dope was a problem, couldn't see that taking Valium was a problem, couldn't see that drinking was a problem, but certainly I knew that helping yourself to pethidine and morphine – injecting drugs – was a problem.

I was very secretive and constantly frightened I was going to get caught, arrested by the police and struck off. I started moving from job to job. I would resolve not to take any more drugs, but then after a couple of drinks after work, something in my head would trigger; something in my brain would say 'This isn't what I want to feel.' I would then get hold of some pethidine, Fortral or morphine from a chemist and that would start off the beginning of a binge that would go on for several weeks or, in some cases, up to several months. I knew I was about to get caught.

The local pharmacist was amazed at the amount of Fortral I was prescribing for 'somebody else's bad back' and reported me to the hospital authorities. I wound up in a treatment centre called Phoenix House, a therapeutic community in south London. You have to be drug-free when you go in, and you work as part of the house, as part of the therapeutic community. You have to do as you're told. You stay there for nine months and learn to identify and deal with feelings in an adult manner. Then you leave and become a normal responsible citizen. And citizenship, of course, included drinking! I am now very aware that a lot of people still leave Phoenix House and develop serious drink problems. Which is exactly what I did.

I left Phoenix after about three months and decided not to work for six months. I told myself this had all happened because I'd been working so hard. I took six months off, lived in Fulham, and started going to pubs on a regular basis, really for the first time since I'd been working for my finals. I went to pubs at lunchtime, and in the evening. I joined the local pool team and developed friendships in the Golden Lion. I still used to hang out with people in the music business and there was a recording studio near the Golden Lion, so I would do recording sessions there and hang around in the pub at lunchtime. Drink really came into my life in a way that struck me as being perfectly acceptable and enjoyable.

My marriage now had ended. I started managing a band and there was a novelty value for them in having a doctor involved. I was not getting on well with my girlfriend and I was drinking quite a lot. I decided I needed to get back to work, so I got a good job doing psychiatric research and started a successful private GP practice with a partner.

My line was I was the guy who'd had the drug problem in the past; I didn't take drugs any more but it was all right to drink record company champagne, and to have the odd line of cocaine, because that wasn't addictive. In the practice we didn't prescribe any drugs inappropriately. If a patient wanted, say, amphetamines, we could recommend a dealer but we were going to be straight, strictly looking after people's well-being. We did very well, mainly looking after people who simply needed vitamins or sleeping pills.

After a couple of years it became very clear to me that actually we weren't seeing anybody who really needed a doctor and it became obvious that either I was going to become a society quack or I was going to have to get out of this. It just wasn't doctoring, and I knew that instinctively.

I liked being around famous people, going to night clubs and riding around in limousines, but I was just freeloading on other people's accounts. I was beginning to think 'I've got to get out of this and start looking towards a career in medicine.' We then lost a lot of money after being fired by a promoter with whom we'd been negotiating for a fee for looking after the crowd at a large rock concert.

I was in a hotel in Vienna when I heard the news and I was fed up at losing face. I had really wanted to do this concert and had organised the medical staff. I just thought 'to hell with it', went out to the nearest hospital, told them some nonsense about needing to get somebody pethidine or Fortral, and they gave me all the drugs I wanted. I went back to the hotel and just sat in my room taking drugs.

Back in England I went on a six-week binge. I raided the pharmacies of all the hospitals with which I was associated and injected what I had raided, sitting in my room in Hackney. In the taking of these drugs it was just 'me having lapsed into my drug problem'. Again. I blamed it on the catastrophe of losing the festival contract. It had embarrassed me, made me look a twit. I just wanted oblivion. I didn't care. Again, I knew I was going to get caught.

I had to resign. I started sleeping on friends' floors, borrowing money, resigned from the psychiatric job and the private practice folded. My partner and I were bickering; I was blaming him for having screwed it up with the promoter while I was away. (He wasn't using; he was very straight.) I was drinking quite a lot. I went back into the pub-at-lunchtime-back-in-the-evening routine and quickly ran out of money. I was very miserable. I did actually check into a hospital for a detox from my opiate habit. When I tried to stop using I suffered withdrawal and I was taking a huge amount of pethidine and my addiction to those soon returned.

It only took a few weeks until I was right back to using boxes and boxes of the stuff. Whereas originally it had taken quite a long time to get up to those sort of doses, this time I was experiencing withdrawal very quickly.

I was just running round on my own in a very sad and chaotic state. I had the bank manager after me and I had no friends left. I really resented my mother telling me I should sort myself out, but she did tell me about a treatment centre in Weston-Super-Mare. She said 'If you want to something useful for yourself, you can go there.' I wound up in this place where they said 'Look Brian, you're not some misunderstood existentialist who likes to live life in the fast lane (things I had been telling myself). You're a very sick man. You might as well think of yourself as someone with an illness. You can call it addiction – whatever you want. But if you carry on taking vodka or Valium or beer or Pethidine or any of these mind-altering drugs, you're going to have problems and you're going to carry on going back to your drug of choice.'

I stayed there for a long time and I quite liked it. I was quite good at working in a group. Having been at Phoenix House I was quite good at solving everyone else's problems but there was no way I thought I had an illness, no way I was going to self-help groups, but I liked a lot of the people and I did see a number of them actually go through a considerable change and they did leave and start going to groups. But I didn't apply that to myself and they threw me out.

I went back to London and carried on drinking for the next two years, got a temporary job, decided to control my drinking and most of the time I stuck to my self-imposed limit, which was actually five bottles of Pils. That is quite a high level for 'controlled drinking' and that was on a regular weekday night. I was working in Hampstead and the pub became increasingly important to me. I wouldn't drink while I was working but at two o'clock, if I knew I was getting off at six, I would start thinking about drink. I would almost run out of the department to the pub where I would gulp down the first few drinks and then settle down to spend the rest of the evening playing pool or space invaders.

Often something would happen. I would get into a fight, get barred from a pub, get arrested for being drunk in the street. Most of the time I was in control and considered to be good fun, but about once a month I would get drunk, become really nasty and thump somebody or insult their wife, being what I considered was outrageously funny, for the sake of the audience. I was having serious problems with alcohol. This went on for about a year. All I knew was

I was getting more and more miserable. I wasn't interested in music anymore. I just worked and went to the pub.

I then heard an advert on the radio asking for doctors to go to Cambodia. There was a relief operation going on that that time and I just knew it was what I wanted to do, not for altruistic reasons, but I just wanted to have some fun. I joined the Red Cross and went off to Thailand with a team of English doctors and nurses. We arrived on the Thai-Cambodian border and it was like a MASH-type situation. We lived in camps and everyone drank heavily in the evenings and chased the nurses. We also worked very hard in the refugee camps.

I was promoted to the grand title of medical co-ordinator of the largest refugee camp on the border at that time. This was quite a powerful job. I would arrive at the refugee camp by six o'clock, always with a hangover, make sure that the shooting had stopped, call in other medical teams, pick up a radio and say 'I want a 70-truck rice convoy and two helicopters here by nine o'clock' and these things would just arrive on time. You just don't get that sort of power working for the National Health Service.

I was in Bangkok at the Red Cross headquarters when the border was attacked by the Vietnamese. I had to fly immediately to Geneva to de-brief. It was June 1980. I arrived in Geneva jet-lagged, hung-over, and angry that I had to leave my team out of the border. (I had really put my heart and soul into the job.) I checked into a hotel and suddenly found myself in a serious state of culture shock. Having been in Asian refugee camps, I was now in Switzerland with cars and affluence and all these clean, well-dressed, wealthy-looking people.

Looking through my wallet, I found the telephone number of somebody with whom I'd been in Broadway Lodge – a girl who now lived in Geneva and I thought 'Great. It would be really nice to talk to her; I won't have to discuss rice convoys'. I rang the number. The maid answered and said 'I'm sorry, she died in a fire at Christmas.' So I hung up, but on the *same* bit of paper was the telephone number of Broadway Lodge. I phoned them.

I just wanted to speak to the director and find out what had happened to this woman. I had been thrown out two years previously. I still owed them thousands of pounds and frankly they weren't going to get it. I expected to be confronted about the money but instead I got this guy who sounded really concerned about *me*. He even said 'How *are* you?' He had heard I was still controlling my drinking. How was that going? I said it was fine and I had rung up to ask what had happened to this woman. He said she had been drinking again and she had set fire to the house.

While I felt very odd at being back in Europe, I felt very drawn to this person at Broadway Lodge who was now being very caring. In that conversation he said 'You've got that same illness she had and if you keep drinking, the same sort of thing will happen to you. Why don't you go to a self-help group meeting?' I just felt very warm that this person didn't hassle me for money or anything and I said 'It's nice to talk to you. I'd like to come and see you sometime.' I actually went to a meeting in Geneva. It was full of theatrical people with cigarette-holders and things. I was there for about ten minutes before I left and carried on doing what I was doing. But in Geneva I began to see very clearly that what I was doing with alcohol was exactly the same as I'd done with any other drugs. It was just much more subtle, much more insidious and actually much more dangerous. It was eroding every aspect of my life and I could see with clarity that if I carried on drinking, by my forties I would have become a burned-out, beaten-up GP somewhere in Australia. This was my rock bottom.

I returned to England and went back to the treatment centre where I wanted to talk to this guy about certain aspects of Buddhism. He just said 'Look. You've got an illness. Doesn't matter whether you take Valium, or whatever, you need to stop drinking and go to meetings'. I really didn't want to hear that. About three days later I was on Hampstead Heath. I'd been up all night, and had drunk three-quarters of a bottle of Scotch while writing a Red Cross report. I thought 'I'll go to the pub and have a half of Guinness and then I'll go home and sleep.'

I was very calm. I knew that if I went to the pub and had that half of Guinness, I would be back in the pub that evening and the whole thing would carry on. So I gritted my teeth and decided I had to do it someone else's way. I knew that I had to stop drinking, but I couldn't see that meetings were going to help. I resigned from the Red Cross and went to the meetings. I hated them. Once I stopped drinking I was just overcome by emotional waves, one minute I was happy, the next minute I was in tears. I was angry. I was having a rotten time, but I made this rather bloody-minded commitment because people said 'Look, if you do this, it can work for you.' For the first three months I just sat at the back of meetings hating everybody. I didn't share, didn't do what was suggested and I felt terrible.

I would skip out at the end of the meeting, go back to the horrible room I was living in, stare up at the ceiling, and wish either that I was dead – or rich and famous. I then met a woman at a meeting whom I quite liked and I went for coffee with her afterwards. She was very nice to me and suggested 'Why don't you try sharing. Just try it.'

So I did. She suggested I get a sponsor and I found that just going to meetings and starting to share somehow helped me to leave the meetings feeling more relaxed. I got involved with my sponsor and started looking at the steps.

After about nine months I went back into treatment and for me it was the single most useful thing I ever did. It taught me how to use meetings, and showed me I wasn't such a bad, useless person at the age of 31. I found that people quite liked me as I was. I didn't have to have a glass of champagne to make people laugh. It became clear to me that I needed to recover from feelings of anger and of inadequacy; that this was all part of the illness, feeling emotional all the time.

I came out of treatment with a clear understanding of the first three steps and I actually had an experience in treatment that made step three a reality, a practical reality that I could somehow tap into in very practical situations. When caught in traffic jams in the rain, that meant I was going to be late, instead of sitting there thinking of three different lies as to why I was late, I would just 'hand it over', I would try to connect with something that made me relax instead of blowing my horn and getting in a hell of a state, making up stories about car crashes.

When I left treatment, I went back to London and I found that a group for drug users was just starting up. Three of us got very involved with this, and went to a service convention in Memphis where they taught us how to set up meetings and we contributed to some of the literature. Then recovery for me began to take off. It started to become fun.

The meetings started to expand and develop. It was a very exciting period and that whole second year was actually a wonderful time. Instead of giving myself a hard time for being 32 and feeling like a kid, I began to lighten up and discover it was actually quite good fun learning how to go to a restaurant and learning all these social skills I had been left without when I stopped drinking. I saw my bank manager and explained what had happened. I took out a loan and started to pay off my debts. I was certainly a slave to meetings and I would go every night. I was enjoying meetings.

It was becoming an adventure. I found that if I kept my priorities in order so that one day at a time I didn't take a drink or a drug and put my recovery first, the rest of my life started to fall into place. My career started to come together and I got back into psychiatry again. I still had pretty difficult relationships with women. They continued into recovery in a similar way to the way they had been when I was drinking and using. They were not grown-up, sensible relationships based on respect. They were very compulsive, very gratification-orientated, and I found that continued for quite a while into recovery. I started to have a lot of fun in my third and fourth years in recovery. Every day something new would happen and I was developing my relationship with God as I understood him and feeling far less uncomfortable about that.

A number of coincidences had happened which I now see as having been to do with some divine plan. (And I really do believe I am on a journey that is actually part of God's will for me.) I failed an examination in psychiatry and felt very hurt about it, very embarrassed, but because I failed this exam it meant that I had to stay where I was for another six months instead of going off to find a job with promotion. I knew I was going to pass the exam next time and on the day I got the result, somebody left. An opening appeared. I slung in an application simply because I was on the spot at the time and got the best job I could possibly have in South London – in a psychiatric hospital. I knew at that point I wanted to start working with addictions and it was actually a tremendous opportunity which had happened because I'd failed an exam. I was comfortable seeing that as part of God's will for me.

I gradually started to practise a form of meditation called Sahata Yoga which has opened up the spiritual side of recovery for me. It involved all sorts of energies that I didn't understand, but I did know that it was free and somehow very pure and connected to the divine. Now I meditate every day, go to India whenever I can and for me it has really enhanced recovery in a wonderful way over the last eight years.

I stayed in South London and continued going to meetings, although my attendance began to lessen. It was becoming important to do other things in my life.

Five years ago I got married, which I really couldn't have done in early recovery, and I inherited a couple of step-children, now teenagers. Four years ago we had a baby girl; three years ago we had twin daughters and things are very good today.

I've always been quite open about being a recovering addict in jobs I've applied for. Certainly people were a bit wary to begin with, but I seem to have stood the test of time and continued to talk sense. The novelty value of working with a recovering alcoholic wears off after a few weeks. It's a bit like working with a vegetarian or Buddhist or someone who just does something slightly differently. I have the difficulties that everyone has to face from time to time – difficulties with my huge family, occasional difficulties with money and so on. But I'm very clear that I have a set of principles that I now live by that help me to deal with life's everyday problems in a way that I never had before.

I was always looking for a spiritual direction. Now I have one. My values have changed quite a lot. I no longer want to be rich and famous, driving around London in open top cars at three in the morning. I really enjoy spending Sunday with my children on Wandsworth Common. I still have areas that I'm not particularly good at – social small talk and I'm still not very comfortable around rich and famous people in the music business. I still get odd flashbacks of behaving outrageously in nightclubs and I'm very clear that I was around them for all the wrong reasons.

I'm still a bit of a lone voice in the psychiatric profession. I'm quite passionate about this model of treatment. I'm still perhaps regarded as a Twelve Step fanatic by my peers but we doctors who are in recovery are more visible and more credible now, standing the test of time. I really do think the field is wide open and I'm excited by what's going on.

I'm very excited about SHARP. I really do think it's one of the most positive things around at the moment. There are still many things we need to do for the families of alcoholics and addicts in this country. I only see it being properly addressed in the United States. There they have residential programmes for family members who really do look at their own illnesses The strain of being around actively-using and actively-drinking people is incredibly complicated and incredibly destructive. I am really impressed by what they're doing over there.

We, in Britain, are quite a way behind. There are a lot of people around giving advice who aren't qualified. This problem does need to be addressed professionally by people who are qualified not only in their own recovery but also professionally as in SHARP. The self-help groups are all wonderful but not professional. Treatment should provide skilled professional help that assists folk in using the self-help groups constructively.

• JOHN WETTON •

◇

*John Wetton is a rock musician who lives in
Hampshire and Los Angeles.*

I was seven when I consciously had my first drink – I used to go to
my grandmother's for lunch. She'd always offer me a cigarette and a
drink after my lunch. I'd have a small glass of port or sherry and away
I'd go.

I don't know whether the feeling came from the alcohol or the environment but I loved it. I was into it from the start. From then on,
alcohol only represented that period and the affection I got from my
grandmother which was some sort of verification. For me it was
security – a feeling of warmth and conviviality. This was in Derby.
When we left for Bournemouth she came with us. She died when I
was about fourteen. I didn't really drink then; in my teens I was not
really that much of a drinker. Occasionally I would have a bit of a
binge with my school mates but it didn't play much of an important
part of my life. I swore I wouldn't be one of those rugby club drinkers; I didn't want to get caught up in that 'Friday night' thing. I was
working in bands all the time I was at school and I was reasonably together so drink didn't play that much of a part.

I wasn't a happy schoolboy. I was a very angry egomaniac with an
inferiority complex. Really bad-tempered, jealous kid. I was very insecure and there was a lot of fear. I wasn't terribly confident. I was
always pleased to get away from wherever I had been; I never
wanted to be in the place I was. Everything else was far more attractive – until I got there and then to me it wasn't attractive at all. It was
the same with girls. That went on all the way through my teens until I
decided to move back to London because I knew that Bournemouth
had its limitations.

When I got there, cocaine was just starting to burgeon. I had no
problem with that one at all. There wasn't any fear of getting addicted
with that! I tried everything, but drugs, other than alcohol, didn't
quite give me what I was looking for, although I quite liked the combination of cocaine and alcohol. You could drink much, much more

without falling over. For me, all my heroes were big drinkers, all the guys that I looked up to all had drink in their lives. And so for me, I didn't see anything wrong with it. As soon as drink became available and I could afford it and my lifestyle did not suffer too much, I jumped in with both feet. And the Speakeasy really was part of my life, it just gave me that power to lose myself. I could drink to excess without feeling terribly ill or anything.

Family, the first band that I joined, seemed to me to be big drinkers, and that was perfect. I didn't see anything at all wrong with that. It didn't matter what night it was – as soon as the recording session was over, we would go out and get completely bombed. It seemed perfectly all right.

It was quite a relief to get into that environment. That was what was so sick. I felt I had come home. I had arrived. It all seemed very glamorous, so romantic. It was what everyone wanted to do. At school I'd dreamed of being in a band that had a top ten record and went out and got drunk every night. That was it. Party to party. It was the fantasy that had no end. In due course, after being with Family for so long, I became so ambitious that I wanted to be in a band that was big in America with me as the singer (Family already had a singer). I joined King Crimson and went to America. My horizons kept broadening. The alcohol kept giving me the confidence, I had a special cocktail that I would have before I went on stage. Several drinks, a small helping of cocaine – terrific.

The problem I had going on stage was that I had to guarantee a certain amount. You can't go on stage in a bad mood and perform well. The only way I knew how to guarantee the mood was to take a certain amount of differing drugs to get me to that place where I wanted to be, before I went on stage. Then I would really have the confidence and I could almost guarantee the mood. If you give anyone a drink, you can almost guarantee that in about five minutes they will change and soften, get a bit more outspoken. With me, I wouldn't be out of control; I would just be about ready to perform. It became an everyday routine.

Had I not had the comfort and confidence-boosting alcohol and drugs, maybe I would not have gone into this way of life. The first thing I wanted to be was a journalist from a very young age, but in that exciting time of the late sixties/early seventies, as music and writing were the two things that I was good at, it had to be one of those. I couldn't see myself getting as far or as quickly as I wanted with writing as I could in the music field. Looking at the competition, I knew that I was as good as they were. Looking at writers, the competition remained much stiffer. I had grown up with people in my class who have actually gone on to become writers; they're good and they're a lot better than I could have been.

As a performer I wanted visibility but I wanted that without the attention. The way I chose to do it was in music which I was competent at, and I could bluster through with the writing. You can use a certain amount of your education and a little bit of natural ability to succeed in writing, say, a three-minute song, but it does not take the same acumen as writing a novel. Of course, my application was zero. I was always impatient, always wanted everything before I got it. By the time I got it, I wanted more. And so it went with alcohol. It happened very quickly with me. Even until 1975, after a couple of years of this matador routine and then a couple of nights getting absolutely wrecked, I was still able to stop for a few days when I had to do something of vast importance.

I'd always bring a drink into the studio. I remember major blackouts in the studio as early as 1974, but nobody seemed to bother much about this. Being carried out of a recording studio was nothing to write home about. People would give you enormous leeway in the music business as long as you came up with the goods. And if you do something good, it is an excuse to go on the rampage. You could defend your lifestyle by saying 'The record's in the charts'. Everything about it was just so reassuring, that one was doing the right thing. Anything short of physical illness or falling over on stage.

The time when it got really out of hand was about 1983. I couldn't stop. I'd wake up in the morning with the shakes and the only way to stop shaking was to have 'the formula'. The formula was then three beers to start the day.

I began a squirrelling of drinks on the road. I would make sure I had enough drink left over from the night before but I had to hide it from myself in case I drank it the night before. Before going to bed I'd have to have another drink. This was about the time when they introduced minibars in hotel rooms – a great gift for alcoholics. I had to be sure I had enough the next morning actually to get me out of bed. Three beers or a half-bottle of wine.

This was when the band was becoming very successful and playing the stadiums. I would wake up at one o'clock. The only thing on my mind was that I had to get a drink. I found it and I drank it and I felt OK. I didn't understand that it was alcohol that was doing it to me when I saw how I looked in the mirror. I was still very angry. I would defend alcohol against everything. I could blame everything else, but alcohol was my friend (or so I thought).

Now I look back on it, I know that I was at fault but in my particular set of circumstances everyone was behaving very badly, even though they may not have been drinking. They were running round like madmen. The pressures of the music business demanded that we do a repeat performance on the *next* record and sell five or six million copies. We were selling enormous numbers of records. There was lots of money.

We, John and Jill, met in 1974, and married in 1987. This is when the drink became a 24-hour-a-day obsession. It was ruining my life. I could not make clear decisions. It was some terrible balance from the first drink in the morning to actually getting out of bed, washed, shaved and planning the next drink. When was *that* going to appear? Would it be lunch time? Would I be able to squeeze one in at the airport or on the plane? And then . . . because you don't perform until about 10 o'clock at night, staying sober enough to do the show. Some nights I wouldn't be. Sometimes I'd get it wrong (I was carrying drink with me all the time).

By now people were aware that I was going over the top. No one else was drinking around me because they were all afraid the same thing would happen to them. Everyone stopped drinking so that I could be the scapegoat. I could be the guy who got all the blame because no one else would back me up. I actually got fired from my own band for being completely irrational. I got angry, of course. It was unjustified as far as I could see; I was in France saying what a lot of bastards they all were. Nobody confronted me with my drinking. Nobody mentioned it.

So this all happened and I was sacked. I still had lots of money so that was all right. It was really a kind of principle. The money continued to come in from royalties so I could afford to drink. It wasn't as if I came down to reality at all. I was still living in a complete fantasy. Three months after the group sacked me, they made the fatal mistake of saying 'We can't do without him; he's got to come back.'

So then I went back into the group, hating them all, but as far as I was concerned, I got back what I wanted. We were in the studio and it became very, very bad. I was obsessed with drink, virtually incapable of doing anything after about 2 o'clock in the afternoon.

The terrible thing about that stage of the game is that you can actually stand there and see it happening to you. You think 'God I'm over the top – I can't do it!' My hands are like jelly but my mind knows what the chords are'. But the co-ordination's gone. Loved ones can't bear seeing us like that. I think I realised by then that I was alcoholic. But no one used the word to me. The worst thing, I think, was my loss of self-respect. I'd seen it happen to other people; I'd seen other people die, people who had gone on the way I had. One dear friend lost his licence, lost his house, lost his wife, and had actually gone insane just before he died. Jill thought on the way back from his funeral 'John will stop now. He's seen what happens'.

One night I was at Tramps nightclub and met David E. again. In my moment of truth, I must have said 'I need help David, please help me, David.' The next morning he called up at about nine o'clock (I had crawled in at five o'clock) and said 'Would you like some assistance? Do you remember what we were talking about last night?' I said I didn't remember. He said 'You were very down and also the worse for wear. I thought you might like to see if there is a way out of it.' I said I didn't remember saying it but he asked 'Can you meet me this afternoon?' I said I didn't think I could – I had 'so many things to do' this afternoon. I had to see an accountant but we agreed to have lunch. He gave me a book, which was the Twelve Steps and Twelve Traditions of AA and told me to go home and read it, and we would go to a meeting.

It was the twelfth step.

It must have been 1984 or 1985. It wasn't until after that I went to AA. My very first meeting was on the Kings Road. It's strange because I went to the same meeting about two months ago and it wasn't anything like I remember. I remember it being huge and people shouting. I stood at the back pretending to be one of the ushers, thinking 'I'm one of them'. I didn't like it immediately. I went to another smaller, more intimate meeting. It wasn't until I got to the Surrey meetings that I started being able to share because they're smaller.

When I went to the meetings I wasn't prepared to learn at all. I didn't want to listen. I just thought: 'This is definitely *not* for me, I'm going back out there!' I went into treatment for three weeks. Basically I was just shamed into submission, I lived with people who had come back from that, who had been in treatment very successfully and been out in the big world and come back. I thought 'I wouldn't want to be like that.' They had been reduced to the point where they had no personality and then built up with another set of building bricks.

The method they used in treatment was to shame you until you had no self-worth at all and then build it up again. I looked at the people who came back. There was something strange about them. But they have compulsory AA meetings at the treatment centre and I liked some of the people. I had spoken to some of them, a couple of the nurses who were recovering alcoholics, and listened to them rather than to the counsellors because I felt immediate identification. A lot of the counsellors weren't alcoholics. The nurses said 'When you leave here, for God's sake go to AA'. And that was the advice I took with me. 'I must get to AA.' I had to find out what me tick, but not going into analysis, which I don't think would have helped my alcoholism. I knew I had to get to AA and find a sponsor. My sponsor, Robin, found me.

I liked the fact that no one was judging. I like the anonymity. That was it. I didn't drink after that. I started working again. The work has come in in just sufficient quantity for me to deal with. Full competence has returned. That was the big fear, that I couldn't write any more. Gradually, in bits and pieces with the help of my sponsor, I did stop drinking. They say if you keep bringing the body along, the brain will eventually follow. I had to find a Higher Power. I had first to separate religion from spirituality before I could get back to believing in God. My higher power now *is* God.

· ASTRID LUNDSTROM WYMAN ·

Astrid Lundstrom Wyman is President and Fund-raising
Director of the Sierra Tucson Foundation.
She lives in London and Arizona.

I was the oldest of five children born in Sweden, and I lived there until I came to England at the age of eighteen. I was at a girls school in Sweden and the biggest thing on Saturday night was to find somebody older to buy alcohol for you. It could be three girls buying a big bottle of vodka and just drinking it to get drunk. I also remember taking painkillers. The ones I liked I tasted the way I would a drink.

I spent a lot of time with my maternal grandparents. Everything was a sin – the cinema, playing cards, make up, boys, everything. I was the focus in the family, the scapegoat. I realised that I was under enormous pressure, supposedly the sensitive, helpless person who had to be taken care of. I was very shy really, until I found alcohol.

When I was eighteen I moved to England to study English. The plan was that I would learn English first and then go to France and Germany to improve my languages before going back to University. I wanted a career. That was my plan.

I met Bill Wyman in London. I was staying with a girlfriend and we were taken to the clubs: the Scotch of St James, the Bag O'Nails, the Speakeasy. After coming from a town of 120,000 people, I leapt straight into a really fast lifestyle. I remember trying purple hearts which I thought were great. I thought this was so wonderful; purple hearts and drinking. I didn't actually consume large quantities of alcohol because I felt happy anyway. I wasn't very promiscuous but I was quite overwhelmed by the whole thing really.

I had never had that much contact with men. It was a little scary, but there was an excitement of course and after only about a week in England I met Bill. I was introduced to him but he didn't interest me one bit. I met him again about two weeks later at a birthday party where we were all smoking pot which I never liked. When I started to go out with Bill I didn't drink because he didn't drink very much. He didn't smoke after that night either because he didn't like it. Then the purple hearts were put away. For a few years I would only have

161

one or two drinks when I went out. Everything was under control.

I was still shy and uncomfortable. I never said a word. I don't know how I lasted as long as I did because I would just sit there. Bill insisted I should go to all the recording sessions and in those days it was so painful for me. I wanted so much to disappear. I was intimidated. It's not as if I was eased into these things. It all happened at once.

In 1970 I went on my first complete tour of Europe. I got very drunk with everybody in Copenhagen and I remember one of the band saying 'Oh Astrid, now you're one of us.' I thought that was so great, because here I was totally accepted. They had all thought I was such a snob. In 1972, on a big American tour, I tried cocaine. The same reaction.

I was always in trouble with Bill because he didn't drink or do drugs, and he didn't like me doing these things. I had to pretend for the next ten years that I wasn't doing drugs. It wasn't easy because when I had taken cocaine I couldn't stop talking. Cocaine really worked for me, as did alcohol. I *used* them. I never drank or did drugs just for the fun of it. They became my tools. I did have social skills but very little practice. The drugs were what helped me with all these things. I was exposed to people and press and, even though Bill was in the background, it was a very public sort of life and it got more like that as the years passed.

I coped with all of it by using drugs and alcohol. And I don't know if I could have made it without them. As much as I'm glad I'm not using drugs and alcohol anymore, I'm grateful in a way for what they taught me. Nobody except the social groups I was in knew anything about my drinking and drug-taking.

By 1976 I was anorexic. I weighed less than six stone and I was put in a clinic where I tried to kill myself, under the influence of some drink and medication. I was brought to a nursing home in England where they gave me prescribed drugs. I was allowed to go out to lunch and in the evening to Tramps. My psychiatrist told me: 'Only one, maximum two, glasses of wine.' He was easy to manipulate.

Until then I had mainly liked wine and champagne. Then I discovered bourbon. Adding it to the prescribed pills was a lethal combination. They, literally, had to push me up the stairs of the clinic at night and when they had got me up there, they would hand me sleeping pills and I would collapse into bed.

I often woke up crazed and trying to smash my room up. I don't know how I lived. Everybody has told me about that time. Six months later my intestines were completely blocked and I was given four days to live. I was put on a drip and taken off all medication. Gradually I recovered but it took a year. I had stayed in the clinic for two months but never quite understood what disorder it was, although the psychiatrist told me it was incurable. I was always going to be like this. It was all to do with having too many feelings and not knowing what to do with them.

Once in a while it would get the better of me and I would be upset. Every time this happened, people would put me in clinics. So the message to me was 'Hold it in. Hold it in.' And really all it was was my addiction; it was me being an alcoholic, not being able to deal with my feelings. That was the only problem I had. I was not a schizophrenic.

In 1980 I was spending a lot of time in America, working on the Jerry Lewis Telethon. It was my first job ever. It just became my whole life for five months. I was so happy. During that time I hardly drank. It was amazing. I was now quite outgoing generally. I would go to parties and have my glass of wine and put it down and forget about it, the way I'd seen normal people drinking and never understood.

When the telethon was over, I was offered my own television show in America. I signed the contract and was going to produce it, but I knew intuitively that I didn't have the training. I went through another bad period, drinking a bit, living by myself, doing opium once in a while and even tried mushrooms a few times. Basically I couldn't cope by myself. That period in Los Angeles was hell for me.

I came back to France, to Bill, and there was no room in our relationship for me to have a job. I was completely unhappy and I started to drink at home all the time. It increased through the years. We would have wine with lunch, wine with dinner and it didn't really stop. In 1982 we left France and came back to the house in Suffolk. As my addiction escalated, Bill's workaholism increased. It was probably because he didn't know how to deal with what was going on with me. We had always had a very wonderful, honest, sharing relationship right from the beginning, but after years of being together it was almost like we stopped working on the relationship. I was using a lot of coke. I couldn't stand just lying there in bed, tense and unable to sleep. I was the rebel. I always felt like this bad person, who always misbehaved.

And when we were on tour I wanted to hang out where all the fun was. Bill would throw away my drugs and my drug-taking would seem incompatible with his straightness. I don't know how he could have put up with any of it. During those years I had two pregnancies that I lost due to the travelling and the drugs.

Then in 1983 Bill said to me: 'I don't think that you can ever be happy if you are with me.' He was absolutely sure that the problem was him. I couldn't even comprehend the idea of my being alone. I'd never been alone in my whole life, ever. I wouldn't have known what to do with myself. I was incapable of walking out in the street by myself. And so I had this incredible tie with Bill which was far harder to recover from than drugs or alcohol.

I went to stay in the house in Suffolk. I would drink a couple of miniatures every morning, and then go riding, take flying lessons or whatever. Then I went off to America where I seemed to be involved with endless projects. I was in LA for a month and came back. From the minute we split up, I drank all the time which I'd never been free to do before. And something shifted finally. After about three months of pain and total despair and blackness, after coming back from LA in May 1983, I started to feel happy. I've never heard anybody else say it but the last few months of my using were the only euphoric recall I have. It was so strange. I felt really happy.

I had two relationships. I got engaged to be married – to an addict of course. I was able to be young again instead of having to be grown up and serious. I had felt from my religious upbringing that here I was a bad person all the time, but now I started to have a fabulous time, looking ten years younger. I had a little taste of a carefree time because the rest of the years when I used drugs it wasn't like that. There had been a purpose behind it – to help me to be me. Now it was just for fun, the way most people seemed to use them all the time.

I was starting to get the DTs. I thought 'I shouldn't really be drinking like this, every day.' So, I stopped. I really had no idea about addiction. Here I was in this big house in Chelsea by myself and I had moments when I felt sad and I'd play Mozart which made me feel even worse. Windows would be open and a bird would seem to fly in. Then I'd be on the telephone and see a snake coming out of the flowerpot. I called Bill and said 'You have to come. There's a snake in my flowerpot. You have to get a knife and stick it in the eye.' He did everything I asked, but of course there wasn't a snake.' He called a doctor who gave me some pills which I took.

That night I was still having the DTs, walls caving in, doors hanging off hinges. It was unbelievable, I was hallucinating for three days. I think I must have started to drink again; wine and champagne. I reached rock bottom in California where I was staying with my English fiancé. Everybody wanted to meet him and there were lunches and parties but I hated it. I couldn't deal with hypocrisy any more. When I used to do drugs, I never could get dishonest. Now I felt unladylike. I used to think 'Drink in the morning! How tacky.' Now I was so disgusted with myself. My boyfriend had to get me a morning drink mixed with orange juice as I wouldn't leave my room to see my friends until I'd had that.

I had used to love being in the sun when I was in California. Now I couldn't take the sunshine. I was so paranoid, my boyfriend would do anything for me. It was getting so pathetic. We could go and sit in a restaurant and drink, and my girlfriend had a bar in the house where we were staying so I would sneak a quick fix from the bottle. When I left the house there were twelve empty bottles.

That month in LA was hell. We were at a party with Helmut Berger and he said 'Astrid! You never used to wear so much make-up!' He pushed me to recovery actually, saying that. That was the final straw. I felt as though I was being found out. My face was starting to show it, I was spending all morning getting ready, throwing up and drinking. I was running out of steam. I didn't have any strength. My face started to feel puffy, and that affected my vanity, my sense of self. My friends were really starting to worry about me.

One day I had that moment of clarity you read about in the Big Book. I woke up, leapt out of bed and said 'That is it. I'm not going to be like this any more. I'm going to do something.' A friend phoned someone who knew about Hazelden and I then had a call saying a place had been found for me. I said 'Yes, I want to go but I want to spend the weekend with my boyfriend who is going to go back to England to stop drinking by himself.' I spent the next four days in hell, drinking the whole time. They were the absolute worst days of my life. I wish I'd gone to Hazelden immediately. It was just a night-mare. There was a going-away lunch for me but I didn't understand really what any of it would mean. I thought it would simply involve not drinking for a while.

I flew to Minnesota and arrived in the middle of the night. I wanted a drink. I was in a panic. I asked for some sleeping pills but of course they didn't give me anything. I started swearing and scream-ing 'I'm leaving.' This happens to everybody but I didn't know that at the time.

I did settle down after a bad period. It was very strict but somehow I did get relief very quickly and also I got a name for what I was. I was not insane. I was an alcoholic.

In time I remembered every drug I'd taken and broke myself of denial. I started to let go. I started to relax and accept and then it all came out. I went to a halfway house and there I had my first spiritual awakening. I had been so upset and miserable, but sitting in a lecture I realised that this was something that was meant to be. I accepted it and that is when my real recovery started.

After four months in Hazelden and the halfway house I went back to London and found my boyfriend still drinking and the house like an opium den. I was petrified in London and I had slips. I went to meetings and back to treatment, and then I finally saw the light at dinner with a girlfriend when she handed me a painkiller. That was the moment when I realised I was going back exactly where I started from. I thought 'This has to stop.' The next day was 13th July 1984 and that is my sobriety date.

Looking back, the next three or four years were pretty hard. I thought then that life was so much better so I *had* to be grateful. Now I had all this fear to deal with. The fear just would not go away but I never doubted the programme. I just believed that it would all come together. I never, ever stopped going to meetings. Whenever I travelled and wherever I went, I always found meetings and went to them. I was and am very, very into the programme.

I also had therapy. After a year and a half, a lot of issues came up that I knew involved more than my alcoholism, things from childhood, unresolved issues. I went back to Hazelden for a ten-day refresher and I just kept working on myself.

My shyness returned of course. People who hadn't known me before my using days wouldn't recognise me. Here I was, this quiet shy person and I knew what they thought about me. One man used to say to his wife 'Why do you want Astrid along. She's so boring.' They were really close friends of mine. She was always asking me questions, always wanting to know about my recovery. She was so curious. Then after *they* had gone into treatment and got into recovery, he made amends. One of the first things he did when he came back to London was to apologise to me. I understood. I was so aware now. I had to let a lot of relationships go.

After the slips it never occurred to me to use again. I never wanted to. My fear has gone. I am so much stronger spiritually and I never feel alone. I am still not going into serious relationships. It's been eight years that I've been alone. For a time I still found emotionally unavailable people attractive. Now, instead of it turning me on, I feel lonely and miserable and sad. I know it's not for me. That is a real shift, the same as when I got that moment of clarity and knew I had to do something about my drinking.

In time I knew intuitively I had to get away from London and

Europe because I was still seeing the same people who had always been there, and although they had always behaved to the best of their ability, I am *not* the same person and now I have to do things differently. When I had come out of treatment I had checked into a hotel in Arizona and looking out at the mountains I knew that I was going to live there. I took an apartment there and it was amazing to be in such a small, manageable place. It had been total panic in London learning to take care of myself. There had been so many gaps in my growth. I hadn't know how to go into a supermarket by myself and I was too embarrassed to admit to all these things.

Now here I am in a small place. Not everybody knows all about me. I can get on and do all the things everybody else takes for granted. Some people might not have the need to fill the gaps but I do. I've been here for two years and I've started to do a lot of work with recovering people which is another reason for staying.

I am now the President of the Sierra Tucson Foundation which has been formed to give scholarships to people with addiction problems who have no money, no access to money and no insurance. I am also the fund raising director and we have, with Ringo's very generous involvement, created an annual fund-raising event – the Ringo Starr Celebrity Weekend. So I am involved with helping people in entertainment, sport and television. We will also work with the American Indians.

As soon as I have time, I will continue the book I have started – not a kiss-and-tell – and I have been asked to do a lecture tour of universities and to do my own range of clothes. I will also write a couple of children's books – I have had ideas for a long time. Also I am now sculpting, so my life is very full and very satisfying and it is all thanks to AA and treatment.

I have a wonderful relationship with Bill. He's been very supportive and I am getting closer to my stepson Stephen again. My friends and family are always there for me. I felt loneliness in early recovery as I was the only one of my friends who went through treatment and there were many painful times as I had to learn new ways to cope and my friends couldn't understand my quietness. Anyway, they *were* supportive as were my family.

It has all been worth it. Recovery has brought me to where I am today – happy, fulfilled and very grateful. I could have died.

· ADDRESS LIST ·

The following organisations can all help with alcohol and other drug misuse.

Al-Anon Family Groups UK, 61 Dover Street, London SE1 4YF. Tel: 071-403 0888. See also local directories under 'Alcoholics (Al-Anon for relatives)'.
Provides a fellowship network of self-help groups which support relatives and friends of problem drinkers.

Alateen, at the above address, provides a similar network of groups for teenage children of problem drinkers.

Alcohol Concern 275 Grays Inn Road, London WC1 8QF. Tel: 071-833 3471.
Aims to change the lack of recognition of the illness and to build public and government support for the growing campaign for safer drinking.

Alcohol Concern Wales Brunel House, 2 Fitzalan Road, Cardiff, CF2 1EB. Tel: 0222-488000.
Same aim as above, but for Wales alone.

Alcoholics Anonymous Head Office UK: PO Box 1, Stonebow House, Stonebow, York YO1 2NT. Tel: 0904-644026.
London Region Telephone Service: 11 Redcliffe Gardens, London SW10 9BG. Tel: 071-352 3001. See also local directories.
Network of self-help groups within which problem drinkers are able to support and help each other.

The Chemical Dependency Centre 11 Redcliffe Gardens, London SW10 9BG. Tel: 071-352 2552.
Provides out-patient and residential care for those suffering from alcohol- and drug-related problems.

Cuan Mhvire 132 Armagh Road, Newry, Co. Down, BT35 6PU. Tel: 0693-62429.
Rehabilitation services for alcoholism and other addictions.

Families Anonymous 310 Finchley Road, London NW3 7AG. Tel: 071-281 8889.
Provides fellowship network for families and friends of drug-dependent people.

Health Education Authority Hamilton House, Mabledon Place, London WC1 9TX. Tel: 071-383 3833.
Government-funded organisation providing health education; its Alcohol Programme promotes 'sensible drinking' and co-ordinates the 'Drinkwise Campaign'.

Health Education Board for Scotland Woodburn House, Canaan Lane, Edinburgh, EH10 4SG. Tel: 031-447 8044.
Undertakes a range of initiatives related to alcohol misuse.

Health Promotion Authority for Wales Brunel House, 2 Fitzalan Road, Cardiff CF2 1EB. Tel: 0222-472472.
Provides information to the public on various health issues including the misuse of alcohol.

Narcotics Anonymous 79 Lots Road, London SW10. Tel: 071-351 6794.
Provides a fellowship network of self-help groups within which drug-dependent people can support and help each other.

Northern Ireland Health Promotion Authority The Beeches, 12 Hampton Manor Drive, Belfast BT7 3EN. Tel: 0232-644811.
Provides information on health-related issues to the general public.

Samaritans London Region: Tel: 071-734 2800. See also local directories.
Provides a 24-hour confidential helpline for anyone in distress or need.

Scottish Council on Alcohol 137-145 Sauchiehall Street, Glasgow G2 3EW. Tel: 041-333 9677.
National organisation dealing with all aspects of alcohol-related problems; has many affiliated local organisations.

SHARP – Self Help Addiction Recovery Programme – 11 Redcliffe Gardens, London SW10 9BG. Tel: 071-352 2552.
Provides a specialist highly structured day programme for clients with drug- and alcohol-related problems and their families.

Treatment Centres and Clinics:

Broadreach House, 465 Tavistock Road, Plymouth, Devon PL6 7HE. Tel: 0752-79000.

Broadway Lodge, Oldmixon Road, Bleadon, Weston-Super-Mare, Avon BS24 9NN. Tel: 0934 812319.

Clouds House, East Knoyle, Wiltshire SP3 6BE. Tel: 0747-830733. Alcoholism and drug dependency treatment centre.

· INDEX ·